TREK

IN THE 24th CENTURY

James Van Hise

PIONEER BOOKSINC

Recently Released Pioneer Books. . .

Library of Congress Cataloging-in-Publication Data
James Van Hise, 1959—

   Trek in the 24th Century: The Next Generation and Deep Space

   1.   Trek in the 24th Century: The Next Generation and Deep Space
           (television, popular culture)
  I. Title

Published by Pioneer Books, Inc., 5715 N. Balsam Rd., Las Vegas, NV, 89130.

First Printing, 1994

PUBLISHER, EDITOR, DESIGNER: Hal Schuster
DESIGN INSPIRATION: Ben Long

COVER ART BY BRUCE WOOD, DESIGN BY HAL SCHUSTER

Interior Color Photos Photo ©1994 Albert L. Ortega

TABLE OF CONTENTS

TREK

IN THE 24th CENTURY

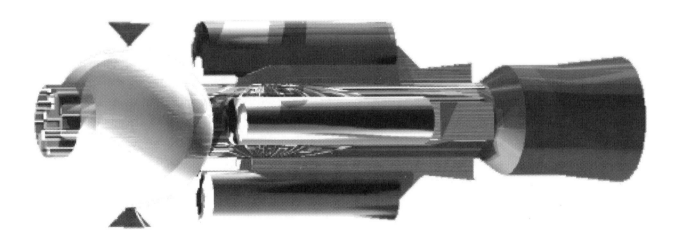

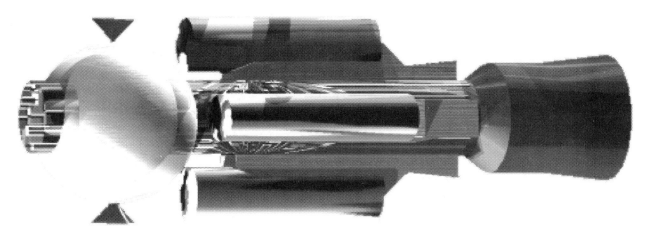

THE SHARED STAR TREK UNIVERSE

The original STAR TREK series dealt with life in the 23rd century. Things were simpler and less complex than the NEXT GENERATION and DEEP SPACE NINE set in the 24th Century. The brave new worlds encountered by the Enterprise-D, commanded by Jean-Luc Picard, and Deep Space Nine, commanded by Benjamin Sisko, are explored against a backdrop in which Klingons have become friends of the Federation while Romulans make up their minds where to stand.

Into this mix comes the Borg, a powerful new enemy from the outside, and the Cardassians, a wily new enemy from inside Federation space. Then there are the Ferengi, a race of businessmen who make any deal for a profit, although the one-dimensional portrayal on THE NEXT GENERATION has been softened on DEEP SPACE NINE.

DEEP SPACE NINE is the first STAR TREK spin-off on the air at the same time as another series. Both NEXT GENERATION and DEEP SPACE NINE occur in the 24th Century. They sometimes overlap. The Cardassians and the Bajorans introduced on NEXT GENERATION are primary elements of DEEP SPACE NINE.

The Ferengi, also introduced on THE NEXT GENERATION, languished as minor players for several years. They were elevated with the appearance of DEEP SPACE NINE.

WHAT LIES INSIDE

This book explores the universe begun with "Encounter At Farpoint," the first NEXT GENERATION episode. This universe grew, expanded, and broadened until it was so laden with riches, some were moved lock, stock, and barrel into the spin-off DEEP SPACE NINE.

The Bajorans are just one of dozens of alien races introduced on NEXT GENERATION. The Cardassians are vile and menacing enough to trouble both the space station, Deep Space Nine, and the Enterprise.

DEEP SPACE NINE added its own part of the galaxy to explore—the Gamma Quadrant. They encounter worlds and cultures as strange as anything Captain Picard found.

Writers used to explore the aliens and ideas of the original 79 episodes of STAR TREK, analyzing and organizing them to exhaustion. That was the 23rd Century version of STAR TREK. Seven years of NEXT GENERATION and two years of DEEP SPACE NINE have produced 200 episodes adding a whole new century to the mythos.

They only peripherally rely on the worlds and aliens introduced on the original STAR TREK. The

Romulans are an outgrowth of what we knew before, but dramatic new twists have been added. The Klingons are virtually unrecognizable. Many new races and characters have been introduced.

This book explores the new territory, a galactic tapestry carefully assembled an episode at a time. From the Borg, who dwarf anything the original STAR TREK faced, to the quirky Ferengi, this is a new universe. It is a realm in which one show can easily cross over to the other for the first time in the history of STAR TREK.

This book is a fabulous road map for those who hadn't realized how complex the 24th Century has become. Turn the pages and explore the many new fables of STAR TREK.

–JAMES VAN HISE

THE NEXT GENERATION AND DEEP SPACE 11

While the Enterprise cruises throughout the galaxy, the space station Deep Space Nine remains firmly in place just this side of the wormhole, waiting for the galaxy to come to them. Is this a drawback of DEEP SPACE NINE or just another way of telling a story? How different are the approaches used in THE NEXT GENERATION and DEEP SPACE NINE? How different are the characters? In their own way, each draws upon strengths of their surroundings.

24TH CENTURY TREK

by Valerie Herd

Picture yourself, a 20th century human, stepping through a time portal into the universe of STAR TREK—THE NEXT GENERATION. Assuming you remain rational at this moment, how would you feel about the prospect of living amongst the humans and other life forms on Picard's ship? Would it be easy to adapt to their way of life? Or might it be easier live on the Deep Space Nine space station?

Those seen aboard the Enterprise-D have sometimes been described as unrealistic, simply "too good to be true." They are accused of not displaying 'normal' human behavioral patterns as they traverse the starry blackness. Instead they boldly offer the hand of friendship to even the most unlikely alien races.

Any intelligent being who threw caution to the wind and responded to the invitation of the Voyager spacecraft to venture to our world would swiftly be strapped to a steel examination table. Meanwhile, the majority of Earth's population would be kept unaware of their visitor's presence, and unhappy fate.

STARFLEET'S ELITE

Human history reveals that mankind has changed very little. As Spock pointed out, the savage beast is still with us, despite our technological leaps. This beast will still be easily called upon by humans three hundred years from now. While Picard and his officers display unusual stoicism in danger, those aboard the Deep Space Nine station react in a more emotional, perhaps more human, way. Their lot is different, perhaps more difficult, given their way of life.

As the series moved into the 1990s, STAR TREK—THE NEXT GEN-ERATION offered several thought-provoking stories showing the crew of the starship Enterprise exer-cising tolerance and understanding in the face of adversity. Their deter-mination to accomplish their mission gained strength with each passing lightyear.

Although the villainous Q pointed out their flaws, the captain and crew of the Enterprise-D appear supe-rior to today's humanity. They display an enviable ability to keep their emo-tions firmly in check.

Fiery, young Captain Kirk was an intelligent, impulsive and passionate human being of the 23rd century calmed by the influence of the Vulcan at his side. Picard prefers diplomacy over quick, vio-lent action. In this, the fic-tional Trek universe reflects current changes in world politics. Although Picard talks to save his ship and crew, today's world leaders face something far more sinister than phaser banks.

If Picard and his crew appear unrealistic, we should take a close look at today's space program. The men and women who live and work together aboard NASA's space shut-tles and Spacelab and Russia's Mir space station are carefully selected for mental health. In many ways they are different from the rest of us, just as those aboard the Enterprise-D would be different from average 24th century humans.

THE HUMAN ADVENTURE

Picard's brother refuses to have a food replicator in his home, and scoffs at the off-world path chosen by Jean-Luc. He is a farmer, very different from his brother (See: "Family"). Earthbound humans of Trek's 24th century, such as he, are similar to 20th century humanity, although their world is at peace.

The view normally shown over the last seven years is 24th century life seen through the eyes of highly trained starfleet officers. If survival through the next few hundred years requires greater tolerance and understanding, THE NEXT GENERATION's portrayal of the 24th century is realistic.

Tales of THE NEXT GENERATION seen from the Starfleet officers' point of view have placed emphasis on the crew's professional lives rather than personal experiences. With the exception of Worf, who often gives in to his Klingon emotions, the humans aboard ship are not often seen in romantic situations; or experiencing the pain of separation from loved ones left on Earth; or displaying jealousy and other inevitable human traits. The glimpses viewers have seen of the crew's private lives, particularly during the last few seasons, confirm that these 24th century humans are closer to 'us' than they originally appeared. The bulk of the weekly episodes could have been taken from the ship's official logs, with private experiences unrecorded.

Television viewers watched Picard's crew meet different races of varying aggression and intelligence. The most intelligent and powerful of these beings, Q, is the one with the most to learn. Perhaps, the series tells the viewer, those devoid of human qualities, good and bad, are least likely to achieve wisdom.

THE MANY SIDES OF LIFE IN SPACE

The tale of the Borg illustrates this message. A seemingly perfect blend of man and machine, the Borg, with the exception of the human-"infected" 'Hugh,' lack compassion. The Borg see(s) nothing wrong in annihilating those who refuse to become part of Borg culture. The advancement of the Borg through Federation territory can be seen both as the classic story of man versus machine, and ethnic cleansing with a futuristically sinister twist.

Trek has always had a tradition of placing today's issues into Trek stories, including torture, racism, ethnic cleansing and environmental warfare. The Cardassians continue the practice. They are a new race of leather-clad, jack-booted humanoid monsters sneering menacingly at Starfleet through cold, unfeeling eyes. The two-part episode with Picard as a Cardassian hostage subjected to torture achieved instant notoriety. Its hard-hitting, gut-wrenching storyline was written with the aid of taped interviews with actual torture victims supplied by Amnesty International.

The captain was not the hero, but a helpless victim. It was painfully obvious to viewers that his tormentors personified the worst of humanity. This story clearly showed that Jean-Luc and his crew are deeply disturbed by the brutality in their universe.

Happily, NEXT GENERATION viewers also witness tales of love, loyalty, family, pain, loss and healing. Episodes show technological achievement and camaraderie in heart-warming, memorable stories written by a thoughtful and caring writing team.

THE NEW CHALLENGES OF DEEP SPACE NINE

DEEP SPACE NINE takes it a step further. Starfleet is a guest on a Cardassian-designed space station, built by Bajoran slave labor. The rules are abstract, more challenging to Commander Sisko. His duty is to insure that things run smoothly.

The possibility of Cardassian attack is more of a threat than to a starship. Sisko, while responding to occasional contact with the Cardassian military with an air of calm and diplomacy, must take each promise with a grain of salt. He knows the sting of forced occupation is strongly felt by the Bajorans who grant permission to the Starfleet officers to remain on the station.

DEEP SPACE NINE shows life in the future from a different viewpoint. Starfleet personnel are as highly skilled as those aboard the Enterprise, but they must live in a stationary structure with unfamiliar technology and sometimes uncooperative computer systems. They must dance to a different tune, that of the Bajoran government. Starfleet and Federation rules further complicate things.

The unknown arrives through the newly discovered wormhole; people living on the station not nearly as compelled toward tolerance and peace as those aboard a Federation starship. Sisko and his crew must remain constantly alert to the possibility of sudden, unexpected violence caused by racial and religious tensions and personality conflicts.

Picard safely adheres to the Federation's Prime Directive. Sisko has to bend it to run the station and prevent the tempers of visiting aliens and the Bajoran rulers from flaring out of control.

SAME PROBLEMS, DIFFERENT DAY

Sisko's job appears more difficult than Picard's. A starship captain completes a mission then moves on to another part of the galaxy and another adventure. Sisko's problems and those who cause them continue to haunt him. While Picard takes each encounter with the unknown easily in his stride, Sisko, though just as cool-headed, often demonstrates an iron-clad resolve. He is quick to pick up the gauntlet as his station cannot fly away to avoid an attacker.

Viewers might conclude it takes a different type of Starfleet officer to run a space station such as Deep Space Nine. Problems occur on a more frequent basis. Life aboard a space station in the 24th century is different from that of a starship crew. Only those on Deep Space Nine who have served aboard a Federation starship are aware of the differences. Those aboard the Enterprise give little thought to life on a space station situated on the edge of the unknown.

One might imagine than an occupant of Deep Space Nine would immediately notice the more tranquil atmosphere aboard a starship, but a starship officer taking shore leave on Deep Space Nine might not notice the strains experienced by its staff. The starship officer would probably focus on the games at Quark's or the activity of the Promenade, so very different from anything seen aboard ship.

Bajorans are gradually recovering from brutal occupation by a military force. They now appear to have found an ally in Starfleet. This does not please former freedom fighters such as Kira Nerys. Many Bajorans don't want to have their planet protected by a fleet dedicated to peaceful contact and exploration. Bajorans struggle with racial hatred of the Cardassians. Most would prefer to exterminate the race.

A CROSS-SECTION OF HUMANITY

During her first few months aboard the space station, Kira learned not all Cardassians are vicious monsters. She also learned to trust the Starfleet officers she serves with.

Sisko always held the trust of the Bajoran people's beloved religious leader, Kai Opaka. This swayed Kira into giving this man a chance to prove himself. Her people might prefer to go it alone, but,

in Sisko, Kira and many other Bajorans know they have one Starfleet human they can fully trust.

Unlike on the Enterprise-D, constant conflict is part of Deep Space Nine. This similarity to 20th century life is one reason for the series' widespread acceptance. Many viewers relate to young Jake Sisko's struggle growing into adulthood, and his reluctance to explain to his father that, despite his father's dreams for him, he does not wish to join Starfleet.

There is also Keiko O'Brien's sadness at giving up her career in Starfleet to live with her husband, Miles, on Deep Space Nine. Despite his complaints, he enjoys tackling the Cardassian-designed computer systems in his care. Keiko now teaches school, putting her diplomatic skills to good use in a classroom filled with children of many racial and religious backgrounds.

The exuberance of brash young doctor, Julian Bashir, can be likened to that of a certain James Kirk of the previous century. Although young and inexperienced, Bashir proves himself extremely capable attending to the needs of various alien races, and adapting to life on a space station far from home.

PAST PROLOGUE

The DEEP SPACE NINE of the 24th century is linked with the Classic STAR TREK timeline. Fans recall the appearance of a three-dimensional chess set on Sisko's desk, talk of a Tellarite vessel's docking at the station, mention of Sarek of Vulcan (now deceased), and the visit by three original Klingons, surgically restored to their former bumpy-headed glory.

THE NEXT GENERA-TION left the small screen at the height of its popularity and, like its prede-cessor, lives on in reruns, as well as venturing to the big screen. DEEP SPACE NINE began with a small-er audience but gained popularity and proved to be a worthy addition to the Trek universe. Future episodes of DEEP SPACE NINE may offer more interaction between the station and Starfleet, offer-ing glimpses into what really makes these futuris-tic humans "tick." As more links are added to the chain created by Gene Roddenberry and contin-ued by Rick Berman and Michael Piller, the STAR TREK universe grows richer, more interesting and realistic.

As a famous 23rd cen-tury Starfleet officer once pointed out: "there are always possibilities."

Dafydd ab Hugh is the author of a recently published STAR TREK—DEEP SPACE NINE novel from Pocket Books and writes here about the unique portrayal of the type of military experience that is Starfleet.

GRASS-EATER TREK: THE STYLE OF STARFLEET

by Dafydd ab Hugh

What would an "alien anthropologist" think if it snuck aboard Deep Space Nine or the starship Enterprise to study the crew members whose adventures we follow each week? This test allows the analyst to back away from a highly personal subject by pretending to be an alien anthropologist who has never before seen or heard the data: what would such an alien think? There is little question; an alien anthropologist would quickly conclude that the crew members had all evolved from herd-dwelling herbivores, "grass-eaters."

The conclusion follows inevitably from their use of violence and their reactions to other people's use of violence. Simply put, the STAR

TREK universe handles violence in the way one would expect from The Far Side's intelligent deer or cows with horn-rimmed glasses.

Many people mistakenly believe that herbivores are placid, non-violent, spending their days peacefully munching the lawn. The image is far from the truth. Herbivores not only have extensive experience as the victims of violence—being stalked, killed, and eaten by carnivores—but many herbivore species engage in violent trials among themselves.

However, the hallmark of grass-eater violence is determinism: to a grass eater, violence either works absolutely, killing the target, or it does not work at all.

PREDATOR EVOLUTION

Consider male giraffes who fight for a mate; they face each other and swing their long necks like clubs, beating each other in turns until one is victorious. Often the losing giraffe's neck is broken, and it is not uncommon for it to die from the injury, sometimes by starvation.

Rabbits fight each other for dominance and mating; the winner continues hitting the loser long after the fight is won, frequently until death results. (Sometimes even death does not stop the fight.)

Grass eaters have little concept of yielding in a fight—as one might expect. Evolutionarily, yielding to a predator results in the animal's death.

Violence itself is so deeply ingrained in us by millions of years of predator evolution that to evolve away from the use of violent force is to evolve away from being human. What is predation but justifiable homicide anyway? Murder justified by the most justifiable cause of all: 'cause I was hungry!

Carnivores generally have a highly developed sense of pack hierarchy decided by a lengthy sequence of combats between the pack members as they grow to adulthood. For this reason, violence among carnivores (including humans) is not always deterministic. Rather than fighting to the death, predators fight until one of them yields. . . whereupon the victor shows mercy, refraining from further attack.

Of course, not all grass-eater battles result in death, and sometimes carnivores do kill other pack members. The general tendency, however, is deterministic violence in the first and dominating violence in the second. Which brings us to the science fiction universe in question here.

THE NATURE OF VIOLENCE

In the TV-land violence of STAR TREK and DEEP SPACE NINE, our alien anthropologist would spot the pattern of violence found in grass eaters, not that found among predators. Violence in that universe—omnipresent, as it is throughout most American television shows—is invariably determinant: it always either works completely or fails utterly.

In the real world, carnivores slowly escalate violent forces, generally to mixed results. Force itself is always a bargain: you can achieve your goal, but only if you are willing to pay a particular price. Sometimes the deal is worthwhile; often it is not.

The most effective tactic of violence, as shown in the works of such writers as Robert A. Heinlein, is to escalate to dominance: real humans must first have a firm and steady goal (as the United States had in World War II and did not have in the moving target in Vietnam). Then the actor attempts to achieve the goal nonviolently.

If rebuffed with violence, he escalates and tries again, continuing to escalate until he finally dominates the opposition and achieves his goal.

This is how a police officer resolves a violent confrontation: if he orders a suspect to the ground but is ignored or resisted, his next response is not to draw his pistol and shoot the offender. There are several procedural, intermediate steps of force escalation between issuing a verbal command and discharging his service weapon.

THE CONCEPT OF RATIONAL ESCALATION

Because real humans evolved from predators (unlike the Federation crew members in STAR TREK shows), they instinctively understand the escalating, give-and-receive nature of violence: war is the extension of diplomacy by violent means, and it, too, follows

a lengthy sequence of intermediate steps, violent and nonviolent, short of war. War can only be justified when a state exhausts all such options short of war.

Escalation of dominance is one characteristic that distinguishes justifiable violence from senseless violence. (Another is whether the goal itself is just, of course.) Even a just cause can result in an unjust use of force, if the force level is inappropriate.

There is no sense of rational escalation of violence on STAR TREK or DEEP SPACE NINE, at least not from the Federation crew members; no sense that anybody understands how to use phasers and photon torpedoes to get what they want. The weapons come into play in a spasmodic series of more-or-less random reactions to stimuli: somebody takes a pot-shot at the station, and Sisko orders return-fire, presumably after thanking his lucky wormhole that the bad guys were bad shots.

Any rational predator (like a Klingon or a Cardassian) approaching an unknown rider in the "vasty deep" of space would already have its shields up and all weapons ready for immediate use. The original series bible for THE NEXT GENERATION discussed this, stating that shields could be assumed to be "up" at all times except for the few seconds it took to transport someone or something.

THE LOGICAL AND THE ILLOGICAL

The series seems to have dropped this wise course—a mistake particularly egregious in DEEP SPACE NINE, where transporting anybody anywhere is rare. In nearly every hostile encounter, the script includes a variation on the following dialogue:

WORF:
Captain, they're powering up their weapons.

PICARD
Shields up, Mr. Worf.

Why in heaven's name were the shields down in the first place? Was the Enterprise crew worried they might offend these unknown aliens by assuming a defensive posture? (And by the way, they're damned lucky the aliens had to "power-up" their weapons before firing. . . imagine if the bad guys used mass-accelerating rail guns: the first indication the Enterprise would have that the aliens were hostile was when a huge uranium slug punched through the hull at several kilometers per second velocity.)

If the other guys are also descended from predators, they ought not take offense if the Federation approaches with shields already up, for all carnivores understand the cautious, fully armed approach of one wild dog

to another in the wilderness. Exposing one's throat before one is sure the other party does not intend to sink his teeth into it is definitely bad form.

VIOLENCE IN STAR TREK

The Enterprise does not take such precautions; and for some odd reason, the fixed site of Deep Space Nine is not ringed with defensive systems. Both ship and station are clearly manned by intelligent, bipedal antelopes who cannot bring themselves to believe they are really in competition for anything in the universe. How else can one explain the take-over of the USS Enterprise by a handful of Ferengi (who themselves undoubtedly evolved from scavengers), or the elaborate unconcern for security on a deep-space station at the edge of the universe, sitting on the lip of a wormhole leading to an unexplored quadrant?

Worse, violence in the STAR TREK universe takes

on an eerie, surreal animation: it becomes an entity apart, a separate being that is the enemy of all good and decent folk. This weird conception (violence as a stalking thing) was explicitly displayed several times in the original series, notably in "Wolf In The Fold" (the Jack The Ripper episode) and "Day Of The Dove" (the show about the little red pinwheel energy creature that fed on the enmity between humans and Klingons).

The manifest became imminent in THE NEXT GENERATION and DEEP SPACE NINE; in a real, human universe peopled by carnivores, Captain Picard would have been court marshaled and shot for revealing to the Romulans that the Federation had invented a cloaking device for moving invisibly through solid rock (as he did in the season 7 episode "Pegasus). It was not his call to determine whether the device did or did not violate the treaty signed between the Federation and Romulus. . . but he was a grass eater, and grass eaters do not stalk and kill their enemies: they nonviolently run away, as the Deer God intended.

Grass eaters have little loyalty to the rest of the herd.

GOING TO EXTREMES

In any event, such an empire as the Federation, controlled by people descended from grass-eaters, rather than meat eaters, cannot phase or modulate its violent response to non-compliance. It responds by spasm, generally with too little force—a phaser shot across the bow, which any enemy would interpret as a badly aimed lethal attack, or attempts to disable the enemy ship's phaser array, the sci-fi equivalent of shooting the pistol from the bad guy's hand.

Inevitably, such nonsense does not work. The Federation deer have no recourse but to launch an all-out, totally committed attack; they have no intermediate modes.

As additional evidence of the grass-eater hypothesis, our alien anthropologist might point out that neither the starship Enterprise nor the Deep Space Nine station appear to have any concept of pack hierarchy, unlike (for example) any contemporary military vessel or base. Although Captain Picard seems firmly in charge of the Enterprise, he makes no decisions: instead, he continually "consults" with his crew, including junior officers who would be no more qualified to advise the captain than would the ship's dog, and then implements their consensus opinion. Sometimes Picard goes further, making his decision on the advice of the ship's bartender, Guinan.

The Enterprise is not run as a military vessel at all: the hierarchy is better modeled by a junior high school, with Picard as principal, Riker as the boy's vice-principal, Worf as a gym teacher who also walks the yard during lunch, Dr. Crusher as the school nurse, and Deanna Troi as the school counselor. Geordi might be a science teacher, and Data is presumably the school science project.

MALL TREK

DEEP SPACE NINE carries to the extreme this herbivorous process of decision-making, which probably stems from the perennial television fantasy of an "unmilitary military" (cf. M*A*S*H, MAJOR DAD, etc.). Here, even the executive officer, Major Kira, is an inexperienced, paramilitary terrorist who was apparently created as an instant-major, a 90-day wonder (like Major Winchester on M*A*S*H), sent to the station to get her out of everyone's hair on Bajor.

There is no hierarchy whatsoever following the executive officer. Unlike the Enterprise, which at least pays lip service to a chain of command, there is nobody on DEEP SPACE NINE who reports directly to Kira and has overall, general responsibility for the station. If the Enterprise is a junior high school, then Deep Space Nine is a Galleria shopping mall, with Sisko as the mall manager sent by the central office, Kira as his local assistant manager, Odo as the mall cop, and everyone else as an employee.

Lieutenant Dax is a science officer and a longtime friend of Commander Sisko; but we have never seen Kira give Dax an order and say, "that's an order, Lieutenant," as Commander Data has said to Worf. In addition, Dax's nebulous responsibilities clearly do not include running the station.

Other than Dax, we have: Bashir the doctor, O'Brien the enlisted chief of operations, and Jake and Nog, the Tom Sawyer and Huck Finn of the deep space Galleria. The other main character is Quark the barhop, who perhaps opened his joint in the mall hoping to be promoted to Mentor, like his counterpart on the Enterprise.

This diffusion of responsibility allows everyone to point at someone else when anything goes wrong—the somewhat more intellectual version of the typical grass-eater response to a predator attack: run away and hope it kills a different member of the herd.

MILITARY SYMBOLS

Unlike a real military unit (or a carnivore pack), if Sisko fell down the turbolift shaft and died, nobody currently on the station would replace him; the home office would undoubtedly send another manager.

The studied rejection of hierarchy leads to some truly silly scenarios. Military rank, the emblem of hierarchy that ought to indicate incrementally increasing dominance, retreats instead to empty honor. In STAR TREK, the insignia of rank itself grows smaller and smaller, becoming nothing more than tiny dots on the collar.

In the grass-eater Federation, a crewman's rate means even less than rank; and nobody has a warfare specialty: one officer is as good as another, and they find no inherent absurdity in the ship's medical officer or psychiatrist taking command of the vessel.

In a recent NEXT GENERATION episode, Deanna Troi finally learned that being in command of a military vessel occasionally means ordering crew members to their deaths. Apparently she never read the manual—it ought to be written on page one. The commanding officer must treat his crew as ordinals, not cardinals; they are not friends or even individuals but positions.

It is hopelessly naive to expect a psychologist to treat the crew as cardinal individuals at all times except when she puts on her Command Duty Officer hat. But then, these officers are herbivores, and perhaps Those Who Graze have little occasion to practice command triage.

CIVILIZED CONSIDERATIONS

That the Federation has not been wiped out by carnivorous neighbors can mean only one thing: Federation totalitarianism is complete, and they are as secure as any "water empire" — a fact also implied by the monstrous Prime Directive, the ultimate in grass-eater arrogance: the Federation must not contaminate native cultures by its own, for the Federation policy would surely overwhelm the "natural development" of any other species! It's such a burden, being the only civilized culture. . . .

The Enterprise may be nearing completion of its seven-year mission, but the herd aboard Deep Space Nine seems about to meet a predatory alien culture that might puncture their illusions of Federation invulnerability: the Dominion. Of all the races in the STAR TREK franchise, perhaps only the Ferengi are fully equipped with the innate understanding of give-and-receive necessary to deal with the Mafia-like Dominion in the Gamma Quadrant.

It would be amusing to return to the STAR TREK universe a hundred years after Picard and Sisko, only to find the Ferengi now control the Alpha Quadrant and have hired the ragged remnants of Starfleet as bodyguards for the Ferengi booty.

Ad astra per acquisitionem!

Called Cardassia Station, it was built as a mining station during the Cardassian occupation of Bajor. With the Cardassians gone it became part of Bajor, a world in desperate need of assistance.

ENTER SPACE STATION DEEP SPACE NINE

by Kay Doty and James Van Hise

"Impossible."

"Too near the Cardassian border."

"It could be useful."

"Not cost effective."

"Bajor is in a state of economic and physical upheaval."

"Too dangerous."

"Could help extend our exploration into space."

"Do we really want to take a chance on another hostile world taking over the station?"

"Administering and restoring the space station would be far less costly than building another one of our own in the area."

"The Bajorans are asking one hell of a lot!"

"Do we have a right to order our people to go that far from their home worlds?"

"How important is a space station, in the outer reaches of the galaxy, to the safe operation of our fleet?"

These were the words voiced when Federation officials met to discuss Bajor's application for membership. The unexpected, and unwelcome, request was accompanied by several stipulations: Starfleet and the Federation would administer the space station, now abandoned by the Cardassians. This arrangement would remain in effect until Bajor could assume the task. A minimum of forty-nine percent of the work force would be Bajoran. The space station would remain Bajoran property and be subject to Bajoran law. Starfleet personnel must abide by the Prime Directive at all times— Bajorans would be exempt.

For reasons no one quite understood, including many Cardassians, Cardassia had suddenly announced the end of their occupation of Bajor. The withdrawal included the space station, leaving vacant the facility built after defeating Bajor a half century earlier.

The Bajoran people entered a state of shock. Most of them had spent their lifetimes fighting to obtain this goal. Yet the swiftness of the unexpected departure of their oppressors robbed them of purpose and direction.

Once they had been united by a common enemy. Now they fought amongst themselves.

The Bajoran economy was devastated. The puppet government proved incapable of restoring order. Most knew little about the space station. Some former freedom fighters believed they could manage the station as Bajor's military outpost, but cooler heads knew better.

SEEKING ANSWERS

The Provisional Government agreed on little. Their meetings frequently ended in discord with no one willing to compromise. The majority reluctantly admitted they lacked the resources to supply the station with needed equipment and personnel. Arming the station against pirates and intruders was impossible. Most wanted no part of a military installation.

The Cardassians had departed, but experienced members of the Council knew Bajor and the valuable space station were ripe for takeover by almost anyone.

Other worlds coveted the station. The Ferengi cast greedy eyes, and the Romulans offered the greatest threat. Something had to be done quickly.

The Federation seemed to offer the only solution. Reluctantly a request for assistance went out. The Bajorans had little to bargain with, but they insisted on ownership of the space station.

The Federation was divided. Administering the station would require funding and personnel. The Cardassians had taken everything that wasn't screwed, nailed or bolted down, and destroyed what they left behind. Shipping lanes were distant; few ships visited Bajor or the station.

TO BE OR NOT TO BE

Federation and Starfleet had to decide whether they needed a space station many light years distant from civilization. Would the costs of operating the station be justified by the benefits?

Each member of the Federation could only look to the history of their own world for answers.

Representatives of Earth turned to such explorers as Marco Polo who journeyed to China in search of new markets, and the adventurers of Britain, who built a vast empire. Christopher Columbus set out to find a quicker route to the Far East, and failed when the American continents got in his way.

Mankind are adventurers, explorers, and scientists. Most have a burning desire to see what is over the next hill, across the great oceans or beyond the next star. Were Federation members any different? The answers for Bajor emerged slowly.

Starfleet divided just as the Federation officials had on this point. Many captains were called in to testify. They swung the decision in Bajor's favor.

A few captains objected, but most were adventurers by their very nature. They were the ones who ventured forth to, ". . . find new worlds, to go where no one had gone before." Little did they realize just how far that would be.

THE BAJORAN QUESTION IS ANSWERED

Discussions at Federation Headquarters ran seven weeks, when a decision had to be made quickly; the final occupation forces were departing leaving Bajor vulnerable.

The final vote garnered the necessary two-thirds majority. The Federation agreed to the terms for the space station, but Bajor would have to wait for Federation membership.

Bajorans rejoiced as the station changed from the hated designation, Cardassia Station, to Deep Space Nine.

In the end, one event—one discovery—proved the correctness of the Federation's decision. Even those members who had been opposed to administering the station or rendering aid to Bajor heaved a secret sigh of relief that their views hadn't prevailed.

A stable wormhole, the only one known to exist, was found in the Bajoran zone. Access to the Gamma Quadrant through the wormhole was a matter of days, not fifty or sixty years.

Two Starfleet Officers, Chief of Operations Miles O'Brien and Science Officer Jadzia Dax, brought about the miracle. Acting on orders from the station's Bajoran first officer, Major Kira Nerys, they performed the near impossible task of moving the unwieldy station to the mouth of the wormhole, all the while resisting an armed Cardassian attack.

THE STATION TRANSFORMED

In a twinkling, the often maligned, ugly duckling Deep Space Nine became one of the crown jewels of the galaxy—the gateway to the Gamma Quadrant. The wormhole didn't hurt the economy either.

Once lackadaisical laborers assigned to clean, repair and remove litter from the shoddy station, found new energy. They strived to make Deep Space Nine a showplace.

Bright colors replaced Cardassian drab. Guest quarters became clean and comfortable, and even the replicators turned out fairly decent food and drinks—most of the time.

Merchants opened a wide variety of new shops and restaurants on the Promenade. Old businesses, including Quark's Place and Garak's tailor shop, prospered.

Ships stopped for supplies and paid docking fees. People came to make deals, gamble and find a bit of romance. As in all times and places, officers and crews who spend long periods of time on ships looked forward to shore leave. Most had money to spend.

FACING THE FUTURE

Deep Space Nine is not utopia. Aggressors must always be repulsed. Criminals with devious agendas will disrupt the smooth operation of the station. Fortunately, most will not factor the station's Constable Odo into their

plans. It seldom takes the stern Odo long to convince these malcontents of the error of their ways and send them packing.

For all of its problems, Deep Space Nine is a shining oasis for all visitors—a haven for the weary and lost as well as the affluent. It may be the Ellis Island of its day, and an important station for Bajor, the Federation and Starfleet. Against great odds, the station is winning respect from friend and foe.

GATEWAY STATION

Deep Space Nine was built eighteen years before the Cardassians relinquished their interests on Bajor. Although utilitarian in design, the product of Cardassian craftsmen is a durable, fully functional space station. The Cardassians had intended to remain on Bajor for a long time.

The station holds seven thousand, although space is tight when this many people are aboard. The

All Good Things

station often operated near peak capacity under Cardassian control as shifts of Bajoran slave laborers were dispatched from one zone of the planet to another.

Gul Dukat, the prefect in charge of Cardassia Station, ruled with an iron hand. He exacted swift punishment. If the perpetrator was unknown, he chose a random Bajoran to punish since he knew all conspired to undermine the Cardassian regime.

Shortly after Odo arrived on the station, Gul Dukat sought him out and made him an offer he couldn't refuse—to become the security chief in charge of Bajoran civilians.

DEN OF INIQUITY

Cardassians sold the wealth of Bajor to other worlds. Business interests paid tribute to the Cardassians to establish themselves on the station and take advantage of the constant traffic through the halls. A huge area dubbed the Promenade became a crossroads of activity.

One of the most popular attractions was Quark's Place. Gambling was rampant but, so long as Quark paid Gul Dukat his weekly stipend, the Cardassian had no interest in Quark's enterprises.

Dukat was less amused by Garak, a Cardassian who made enemies on the homeworld and found it healthier to relocate to the Bajoran space station.

The Promenade quickly became a bazaar of the bizarre where visitors could gamble huge amounts of money or buy hours of preprogrammed pleasures in the holosuites. They were said to contain fourteen different types of sexual programs, depending on how many appendages one preferred

one's holographic paramour to have.

Before leaving, the Cardassians stripped the station. Much was altered to suit the tastes and discretion of the Federation when they took over.

FEDERATION/BAJORAN ALLIANCE

Some businesses fled along with the Cardassian evacuation. Others remained, including Garak, the only Cardassian left on the station or Bajor.

Commander Sisko also talked (or coerced) Quark into remaining, an unhappy arrangement for the Ferengi businessman. Then came the discovery of the wormhole, making the station more popular than ever.

Under the Federation/Bajor alliance, three hundred personnel live aboard the station and five or six ships arrive each week, some with a large complement of ship's crew and passengers. Even visitors from the Gamma Quadrant bring trinkets and artifacts which Quark often takes in exchange for credit on his gambling tables, holosuites and Dabo girls.

Odo chose to remain in his position of constable. He is less willing to allow Quark leeway since the Ferengi no longer bribes Odo's superiors to look the other way. Quark considers this unfair as it makes it much more difficult for him to earn a living.

INSIDE
DEEP SPACE NINE

The space station is divided into nineteen sections with a Habitat Ring for the main living quarters. The extensive guest quarters are spread throughout the rest of the station.

The Cardassians built a durable station from the metal Duranium. It is equipped with shields that can withstand a limited concentrated phaser barrage. The Cardassians, confident in their numbers, didn't believe it necessary to build the station to survive a war, only the best efforts of Bajoran terrorists.

In the nearly two years since the discovery of the Bajoran wormhole, commerce in the region has increased dramatically although trade routes to the Gamma Quadrant are still being established. The only race to make major inroads on this front are the Ferengi.

Staff aboard the station includes a cross-section of Federation species, among them a Trill (Jadzia Dax), a Bajoran (Kira Nerys), humans (Dr. Julian Bashir, Chief of Operations Miles O'Brien, as well as Commander Benjamin Sisko) and the aforementioned Odo, the only known shape-shifter in the Alpha Quadrant.

Once a region of space ignored by all except the Cardassians, Bajor and its space station Deep Space Nine now sit at the gateway to the Gamma Quadrant. All the mystery and wonder of a new age of exploration lie ahead.

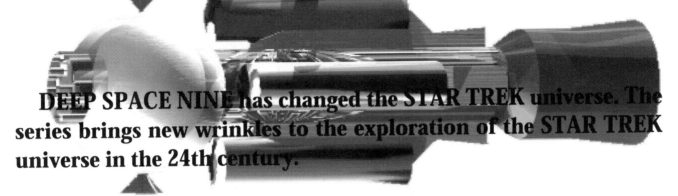

DEEP SPACE NINE has changed the STAR TREK universe. The series brings new wrinkles to the exploration of the STAR TREK universe in the 24th century.

IS THERE A PLACE FOR DEEP SPACE NINE IN THE STAR TREK UNIVERSE?

by Kay Doty

Since the earliest days of Classic Trek, references have been made to space stations—but seldom has one been shown. The subject was almost totally ignored.

In the original series' first season, there is a scene in an office on Starbase 6 ("The Menagerie"). In another episode the crew beamed to Starfleet base Cestus III only to find it virtually destroyed ("Arena"). Kirk's trial for the apparent death of Ben Finney was held on Starbase 12, but the action all took place in the courtroom ("Court Martial").

A stop was made at a penal colony ("Dagger Of The Mind") but that hardly qualifies as a Starbase. The series never gave a view of a station as more than the setting for the action.

Only one significant visit to a space station occurred during the second season. Crew members from the Enterprise and a Klingon ship mixed it up in a barroom brawl, while Kirk was engulfed by little furry animals in the storage section ("The Trouble With Tribbles"). No Starbases appeared during the final season, although the Enterprise stopped at the insane asylum on Elba II ("Whom Gods Destroy").

Budget limitations of the first STAR TREK series may have prohibited more appearances of starbases. However Starbase didn't fare much better in THE NEXT GENERATION.

The Enterprise stopped at Starbase 74 for holodeck repairs ("11001001"), and Starbase 67 for a general overhaul ("Disaster"). Picard and Wesley also traveled to Starbase 515 where the Captain underwent a heart implant while young Crusher participated in an academy exam ("Samaritan Snare"). Fans were treated to a dining room scene at Starfleet Command ("Conspiracy") and a chance to get a good look at Starfleet Academy ("The First Duty").

ENTER DEEP SPACE NINE

While none of these episodes showed fans a Starbase, the numbers used, such as 515, indicated there must be many scattered throughout the galaxy. They are much like the old stagecoach stations dotting western America during the last half of the Nineteenth Century—a convenient stop for new horses (i.e., dilithium crystals), a plate of beans or mulligan stew (a meal which hasn't come from a replicator), or just a chance to relax on solid ground (not programmed in a holodeck).

Until DEEP SPACE NINE no information was advanced as to how these stations were built or acquired. Did the Federation negotiate with other worlds, or were they just set up on a vacant aster-oid or planet? Perhaps a mapping expedition found an ideal location near a shipping line and ordered a construction crew to start building.

Other unanswered questions included what materials were used and who designed the bases. Did every starbase have distinctive plans or were they built to Federation specifications—much as WalMart stores or Burger King restaurants?

STAR TREK novels and fan fiction also offered little mention of starbases, and almost no description. DEEP SPACE NINE finally revealed these important members of the Federation family. Questions are finally being answered. Viewers learn what Deep Space Nine looks like, its size, who built it, how and why. Most important of all, we know its history.

A NEW VIEW OF THE 24TH CENTURY

The Cardassians designed and built Deep

Space Nine. It is interesting to speculate how it compares to a Federation station of similar size and age. Would the shops, entertainment facilities and tourist attractions be similar?

DEEP SPACE NINE has given viewers an exciting new look at their favorite 24th century universe.

Some believe there can be no STAR TREK without the Enterprise, no way "... go where no one has gone before." As the series nears the end of its second season, many episodes have occurred off-station, including much of "Emissary," the two hour premiere.

"Dax" contained off-station scenes, as did "Vortex." In the latter, Odo tried to return an unwilling prisoner to his home world on the other side of the wormhole, when their runabout was attacked and they were forced to land.

STAR TOURS

Sisko, Kira and Bashir took Bajoran spiritual leader Kai Opaka on a tour of the wormhole in "Battlelines." They crash-landed on a planet engaged in an unending civil war. Opaka was killed during the fighting, and later revived. However, unable to live if she left the planet, the Kai was undaunted, saying her work would continue among the people of that world.

In the light-hearted episode "The Storyteller," Bashir and O'Brien shared an adventure in a small Bajoran village. Other episodes also showed brief off-station scenes.

Not bad for a short first season.

The three-part opening of season two offered a number of action scenes on Bajor. Other action has included the near-murder of Bashir and O'Brien on a supposedly friendly plan-

et, and Sisko and O'Brien held prisoner on a primitive world. As this is written, every major character except Jake and Keiko have had off-station adventures. There will continue to be an abundance of action in places other than the space station.

DEEP SPACE NINE demonstrated another way to tell a STAR TREK story. You don't have to "boldly go where no man has gone before" to discover adventure. Exploring a new nearby civilization offers opportunities as well. The stories differ from previous STAR TREK adventures, but they are STAR TREK nonetheless.

Until 1987 there was only one STAR TREK. THE NEXT GENERATION raised it to two, and now there are three. Suddenly the opportunity arose to do something new—crossovers. Now, with two different STAR TREK's sharing the 24th Century, it is inevitable they meet.

THE NEXT GENERATION MEETS DEEP SPACE NINE

January 1993 marked the first time two different STAR TREK series aired in first run at the same time. STAR TREK—THE NEXT GENERATION was used to introduce STAR TREK—DEEP SPACE NINE.

Although initial reports indicated that the whole cast of THE NEXT GENERATION would appear in the DEEP SPACE NINE premiere, this didn't prove true. When "The Emissary" aired there were just two guest stars—Captain Picard and the Enterprise.

Captain Picard featured in an intricate backstory when the wife of Benjamin Sisko died in battle against the Borg at Wolf 359 as 40 Federation starships were destroyed. As the new series opened, a couple of years have passed since this encounter. It is known the Borg were assisted by Locutus, the Borg name given to

Jean-Luc Picard when he was captured and brainwashed.

Picard gave the Borg knowledge of Starfleet vessels. Everyone in the Battle of Wolf 359 wondered how different the outcome would have been without Picard.

Although Picard was cleared of wrongdoing, he still feels guilt. Sisko is angry at Picard for fighting on the side of the Borg.

Captain Picard confronts the equally forceful Commander Sisko. Although Jean-Luc outranks Ben, Sisko is never subservient. He comes close to insubordination dealing with Picard, but Jean-Luc understands Sisko's resentment.

A FATEFUL ENCOUNTER

"The Emissary," the premiere episode of DEEP SPACE NINE, opens with a teaser linking it to THE NEXT GENERATION. Picard/Locutus appears on a viewscreen demanding the surrender of Federation forces. On the battle bridge of the USS Saratoga, Lieutenant Commander Benjamin Sisko reacts to the ultimatum. This is the first appearance of Sisko, viewed in the heat of battle aboard a doomed ship in the now-historic encounter.

"The Best Of Both Worlds—Part 2" showed the aftermath of the battle when the Enterprise arrived too late to prevent the massacre or aid the fleet. The portrayal from the point of view of those who went down to defeat before the Borg (and Locutus) is a new look at a popular story.

Several Starfleet vessels move in on the Borg cube to attack, but are devastated by the Borg. The Borg drain the shields of Ben Sisko's USS Saratoga, then fire a blast shaking the bridge, hurling debris amid smoke from the explosion. Sisko is one of only two bridge crew members to survive.

With an evacuation underway, Sisko fights to find his wife and son. He finds Jake, unconscious but alive; his wife Jennifer is dead. Sisko leaves her body behind when he flees with his son in an escape pod.

HAUNTED BY THE PAST

Three years pass before Sisko is promoted and transferred to Deep Space Nine. The memory of his wife's death remains vivid even though the Borg ship responsible was destroyed.

The Enterprise arrives at Deep Space Nine to deliver the operations staff, including Miles O'Brien. O'Brien is another link in the crossover. He has been on THE NEXT GENERATION since the first season.

Mid-way through TNG season six he switched shows, joining the regulars aboard space station Deep Space Nine. He is the only previously established character in the cast, but some of the newcomers, particularly Sisko, were established in the viewer mind by the conclusion of "The Emissary."

Sisko avoids meeting Picard aboard the Enterprise for a briefing until he is reminded. When Sisko enters, Jean-Luc is unaware of their shared background.

Sisko says they've met before, which leaves Picard at a loss. When Sisko mentions the Battle of Wolf 359, Picard withdraws. Sisko is curt and chilly.

The scene communicates the discomfort of Jean-Luc. Sisko objects to posting to the station, saying he hoped to return to civilian duty and spend more time with his motherless son, Picard doesn't argue. Picard only says that he'll start lining up a replacement.

TURNING POINT

Picard is seen again when O'Brien prepares to leave the Enterprise for new quarters on the space station. O'Brien hopes to slip away without notice, but Picard insists on operating the transporter.

This scene forms an interesting counterpoint to the one in which Picard received a very cold reception from Sisko. O'Brien says good-bye to his commander still aware of Picard's complicity in the deadly Battle of Wolf 359, but harbors no ill will.

Of course, O'Brien lost no loved one at the hands of the Borg, but it's more than that. Ben Sisko can't release the pain of his wife's death and needs to blame someone. It doesn't matter to him that Picard was brainwashed by the Borg; Picard's presence on the vessel that attacked the Saratoga makes him the target.

During Sisko's encounter with the Prophets inside the wormhole, the alien entities adopt forms from Sisko's memories. Picard's form forces Ben to repeatedly confront his feelings, just as the Prophets point out Sisko keeps bringing himself back to the scene of his wife's death. Sisko dwells on the memory instead of getting on with his life to help Jake grow up.

BRIEF ENCOUNTERS

After his encounter with the Prophets, Sisko comes to terms with his feelings and releases the ill will towards Captain Picard. When next they meet, Picard is ready for another cold reception but is surprised when Ben Sisko reacts differently. Sisko wants command of Deep Space Nine, so he and Picard part on good at last.

Viewers wonder why Picard accepts Sisko's change so readily. First an unfriendly Sisko didn't want the position, then a suddenly friendly Sisko wants command of Deep Space Nine. To Picard, this limited exposure made Sisko appear manic-depressive, possessing little devotion to duty. STAR TREK fails to ask these questions.

The other crossover between NEXT GENERATION and DEEP SPACE NINE occurred a few weeks later in a two-part NEXT GENERATION episode. It wasn't as intense or involving as "The Emissary."

"Birthright" opens on Deep Space Nine as the Enterprise returns to assist the Bajorans. Worf beams aboard the space station. He is minding his own business on the Promenade when he's approached by an Yridian named Jaglom Shrek. He claims to have information about Worf's long dead father as Worf leaves on a private mission far from Deep Space Nine.

DATA AND THE DOCTOR

If Worf's visit to the space station is brief, it again establishes it as a possible way-station. One of the staff of the space station also visits the Enterprise during its stopover.

Dr. Julian Bashir visited the Enterprise sickbay to examine the facilities aboard a galaxy class starship. He needs advanced equipment to analyze an unusual alien mechanism. At first, Data questions Dr. Bashir's presence in the lab, but Dr. Bashir soon puts him at ease.

Data and Geordi assist Dr. Bashir in his researches, establishing another positive link between the two series. Bashir's strange artifact emits a beam that strikes Data and triggers a dream program.

Julian is a catalyst in the events in an interesting guest appearance. As a result, Data discovers an important new element of

himself enabling him to experience a common human attribute—dreaming.

After these two crossovers early in the first season of DEEP SPACE NINE, the shows followed their own independent routes. They use common elements of the 24th Century STAR TREK universe to explore different new worlds and civilizations.

No new crossovers have been announced. There may be a brief appearance of Deep Space Nine in the upcoming film STAR TREK: GENERATIONS, resulting in a real first—a triple crossover featuring characters from all three STAR TREK series. The minor element would demonstrate the possibilities interweaving the three shows in the same STAR TREK universe.

How do DEEP SPACE NINE and THE NEXT GENERATION deal with alien races? It all comes down to facing the consequences.

HOW DEEP SPACE NINE AND THE NEXT GENERATION EXPLORE THE PSYCHOLOGY OF ALIEN RACES

by Charles A. Gramlich

Good science fiction is character driven. It is about interactions between humans and other humans, humans and technology, and humans and aliens. STAR TREK has always offered good examples of this kind of storytelling. All three series produced characters that could be used as case studies in human psychology.

Nowhere has the everyday psychology of alien races been explored better than on DEEP SPACE NINE. The latest series takes place on a space station rather than a space ship. The crew of Deep Space Nine has to deal with a diverse population.

The Enterprise is nomadic. It is more homogeneous than Deep Space Nine, and moves on when in the aftermath of a crisis. There is no such escape for Deep Space Nine. This marks the fundamental difference in the two current series. Benjamin Sisko and his crew deal with both conflict and its aftermath, including the rebuilding that follows. They confront, cajole and commiserate with alien races every day. The interactions reveal the true psychology of people.

REIGN OF TERROR

DEEP SPACE NINE has advantages over THE NEXT GENERATION in its ability to portray the psychology of alien peoples. The portrayal of the Cardassian dominion over the planet Bajor offers an interesting contrast.

Several episodes of THE NEXT GENERATION involved Cardassians, but only one or two show their relationship with Bajor. The domination left psychological wounds both races. These can only be hinted at in the rapidly changing background of THE NEXT GENERATION.

DEEP SPACE NINE better reveals the consequences of the subjugation of one race by another. The wounds are reopened, treated and perhaps healed. They can be understood better.

An interesting quote near the beginning of the book THE MICRO-COLONY by Gordon Williams touches on the Cardassian/Bajoran condition. It reads: "There is no psychology practiced in this dark hole in the ground, no subtle breaking down of the will. I am simply going to kick the truth out of you. Think about that."

This statement bludgeons, but the last line of the quote actually gives the lie to the first. Forcing someone to think about the approach of pain is a tool of psychological terror. The tool that has been used by conquerors throughout human history, from the skull pyramids of Tamerlane to the cattle cars of Hitler. In the universe of DEEP SPACE NINE and THE NEXT GENERATION, terror is a tool of Romulans, Klingons and, most recently, Cardassians.

THE MACHINERY OF CONQUEST

THE NEXT GENERATION shows Bajoran hatred and Cardassian contempt. DEEP SPACE NINE shows the roots of these emotions anchored firmly in the soil of terror. Only DEEP SPACE NINE revealed the depth of pain experienced by the Bajorans.

An intelligent conqueror learns to turn the strengths of its enemies against them. The conqueror instills fear. Terror oils the machinery of conquest.

When one man fears death and another fears his own cowardice, when one fears losing his livelihood and another fears being turned over for torture by his brother, his wife, or his son, then thoughts of resistance are set aside. The hatred and bile that fills Bajorans on DEEP SPACE NINE is testament to the power of psychological manipulations. Hatred always contains an element of self-loathing.

Men and women dominated by beating and torture hate themselves as well as their tormentors. An intelligent being questions whether it could have resisted harder. It questions its own cowardice and inferiority. Question follows question until a cascade of doubt sweeps aside self-esteem.

Attempts to recoup self-respect are met with terror, beatings and torture. Emotions are hidden, then dug up years later. This is what has happened on Bajor.

A QUESTION OF CONSCIENCE

Even as Bajorans suffered, many Cardassians experienced their own agonies. DEEP SPACE NINE shows the agonies with richness of detail THE NEXT GENERATION is unable to match.

Although Bajorans—and perhaps much of Starfleet as well—would classify Cardassians as bullies, the actual situation revealed on DEEP SPACE NINE is much more complex. Several episodes make it clear that not all Cardassians approved of their race's actions on Bajor.

The architecture of the Cardassian-built space station suggests a deep and convoluted psyche within the Cardassian people. Gray and brooding mass is gentled by curves. Yet those curves are inwardly turned.

A view of Deep Space Nine from above or below shows three elongated fingers closing into a fist, or a three-pronged forceps moving to probe a wound. There is strict order and discipline overlaid by chaos and fractal anger. The sense is schizophrenic in its original meaning, a splitting.

The Cardassian experience on Bajor was a difficult one. Any conqueror must go through mental contortions to justify abuse and dominance of another people. They must see their enemy as deserving of punishment.

As they push their enemy towards inferiority, they develop a corresponding attitude of superiority. Being superior creates its own internal pressures.

Sick guards beat prisoners out of fun, but you don't find an entire race of such beings. As in our current world, people act out of complex motives. They are not likely to define themselves as evil beasts who delight in torture. Their actions become not only acceptable but necessary. The conquerors produce psychological damage to their own psyches.

IDENTITY CONFLICT

Terror extracts a toll from conqueror as well as conquered. This was well illustrated in two recent episodes of DEEP SPACE NINE.

"Duet" introduced a Cardassian filing clerk who had worked in a Bajoran prison camp during the occupation. At first he looked like the commander of the camp, an individual considered by Bajorans to be a war criminal.

Major Kira was assigned to investigate. She believed this Cardassian to be the very embodiment of Bajoran suffering. Our clerk played his role expertly, dissembling when it was clear his lies must be revealed, launching into Hitlerian tirades designed to turn Bajoran hearts against him.

Kira Nerys, afloat in her own pain, wanted to believe the Cardassian guilty. She desperately wanted to find a focus for old anger, but small inconsistencies kept showing up.

The Cardassian was infected with a virus that could only be contracted by someone at the prison camp, but it turned out the camp commander was on Cardassia when the disease broke out on Bajor. They discovered evidence the fellow had undergone cosmetic surgery yet he looked exactly like the camp commander. Gradually the filing clerk was revealed beneath the persona of a Cardassian overlord and butcher.

MURDERING THE SYMBOL

Why did this rather unimportant individual go through the physical pain of altering his appearance? Why did he deliberately expose himself to capture by the Bajorans? The answer lies in cold nights spent in his room at the prison camp, on his bed with hands over his ears to block out the screams. Those screams became memories that would not leave him. When eventually he could not stand it any longer, he became the Cardassian commander.

The clerk's motives seem confused. He wanted to suffer for having done nothing to stop the torture. He wanted to give the Bajorans a chance for vengeance by offering himself to their anger. He wanted his trial for war crimes to force all of Cardassia to face the things done on Bajor.

At story's end, the Bajoran Major, Kira, saw through to the essential humanity of the Cardassian. She felt sympathy. The fellow was released to be returned home, before another Bajoran knifed him in the back. Told he had killed the wrong individual, the Bajoran responded that any Cardassian was right to kill. Being Cardassian was enough.

The use of terror destroyed both conqueror and conquered.

TEACHING SELF-HATRED

Another episode of DEEP SPACE NINE, "Cardassians," featured a young Cardassian war orphan adopted and raised by Bajoran parents. Offered a chance to return to Cardassia and his biological father, the youth recoiled in horror. Though his Bajoran parents professed to love him—and though in truth they seemed to do so—they had taught him to hate everything of his own race.

The guilt is not theirs alone. A Cardassia that used torture, and left behind some of its own children when it retreated, carries its share of blame. Blame doesn't change that the boy's Cardassian father was devastated by his son's hatred. It doesn't change the need for the boy to work through his own equivalent of torture.

It will take decades, perhaps centuries, of freedom to erase psychological damage done to Bajoran by Cardassian. The occupation ultimately produces great disruption for the Cardassians as well.

Their society is driven apart. Do they own up to their guilt and make reparations to the Bajorans, or do they suppress, and even repress, their role in the systematic exploitation of another people?

The first option leads to social upheaval. Military heroes will stand trial for war crimes; attitudes instilled through long term use of terror must be uprooted. Changes come only with immense struggle, often violence.

The second option allows the Cardassians to avoid ripping apart the weave of their society, but leaves a callus on their collective souls. Such societies stagnate.

The Cardassian character revealed on DEEP SPACE NINE suggests they will choose the first option, to confront and correct the horror their actions created on Bajor. When Cardassian fathers love their sons, and Cardassian filing clerks grieve for the pain of another race, the seeds of a better future are sewn. Terror cannot compete against such strengths.

Conquerors and conquered are destroyed, then rebuilt stronger than before. THE NEXT GENERATION offers only glimpses of the forces that impel such change. DEEP SPACE NINE shows each detail in the Cardassian and Bajoran recreation.

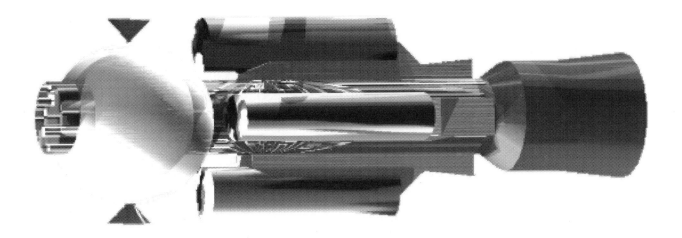

CARDASSIANS: THE NEW MENACE

THE NEXT GENERATION elevated the Klingons from one-dimensional villains to genuine characters with a culture and personality. STAR TREK still needed a villain.

The Ferengi were introduced for that purpose, but they proved so laughable they were quickly relegated to comedy relief.

The Romulans were then promoted from standby to primary villain, although it was shown that not all Romulans are empire builders. Their activities are confined to the Neutral Zone by treaty. Not even an aborted attempt to invade Vulcan established them as true series villains.

THE NEXT GENERATION needed a new race without a complicated preexisting background. The Cardassians emerged in the fourth season episode "The Wounded." [See episode #86 in TREK: THE NEXT GENERATION, Pioneer Books.]

The episode, written by Jeri Taylor (from a story by Stuart Charno, Sara Charno and Cy Chernak), opens with the Enterprise being notified the Federation treaty with the Cardassians has been broken by the USS Phoenix. This is the first mention of the Cardassians. The viewer quickly learns that the Federation and the Cardassians had been at war just a few years before. Since this is fourth season of THE NEXT GENERATION, it can be assumed that the war ended immediately before the series began.

The initial story idea portrays the aftermath of war as sworn enemies learn to coexist. On a more personal level, the story focuses on Captain Maxwell, a man whose family was slain by the Cardassians during the bitter conflict.

When Maxwell learns the Cardassians are secretly rearming in defiance of the armistice, he decides to punish them. This causes Maxwell's downfall when he fails to inform Starfleet and proceeds on his own.

Maxwell has a nervous breakdown when confronted with Cardassian treachery. He relives his personal horrors of the recent war and wants to exact vengeance.

THE TRUTH BEHIND THE TREACHERY

Initially the Cardassians seem to be innocent victims of Maxwell's madness. "The Wounded" is really about Maxwell and how the Enterprise stops his one vessel war against the Cardassians.

Cardassian observers accompany Picard aboard the Enterprise. The delegation includes Gul Macet, played by Marc Alaimo. Alaimo would continue to play Cardassians, establishing himself as Gul Dukat (seen on several episodes of DEEP SPACE NINE).

The Phoenix destroys Cardassian ships and could pull the Federation into war. Chief O'Brien, who once served under Maxwell, doesn't like Cardassians either. They remind him of the only time he had to kill, when he fought a Cardassian in hand-to-hand combat.

O'Brien overcomes his feelings and talks Maxwell into surrendering for the good of the Federation. O'Brien and Maxwell both know the horrors that will come with another war.

With Maxwell's surrender the story takes a strange twist. Picard reveals he believes the Cardassian freighter Maxwell planned to blow up contains illegal armaments. He warns Gul Macet that the Federation will be watching.

This sudden change in the portrayal of the Cardassians from victims to conspirators sets the stage for their subsequent emergence as villains in the new galactic order. The next time the Cardassians appear is in the fifth season. This time they are groomed for the much larger role they play in DEEP SPACE NINE.

ENTER THE BAJORANS

"Ensign Ro," written by Michael Piller from a story by Rick Berman and Michael Piller, introduces the Bajorans. Bajor is under the domination of Cardassia. Bajoran terrorists actively bedevil their conquerors.

The premiere terrorist is Orta. When an attack on a Federation colony is blamed on Orta, Admiral Kennelly orders the Enterprise to bring him in. A Bajoran imprisoned on unrelated charges is released and assigned to the Enterprise.

Through this Bajoran woman, Ensign Ro, the viewer gains further insight into Cardassians. Ro Laren grew up in a refugee camp and, as a child, saw her father executed by Cardassians.

"The Wounded" had showed the Cardassians from the point of view of a man ruthlessly victimized during wartime. Ensign Ro offers the viewpoint of a woman displaced from her home world by a conquering race.

The episode also shows a Bajoran refugee camp on Garon II, where people live in crushing poverty. Picard is moved by what he sees and offers his aid. Unfortunately, because the Federation and Cardassia have a treaty, and Bajor is a nonaligned world, Starfleet is not supposed to take direct action.

Starfleet starts to rethink this policy when it is revealed that Orta and his gang of Bajoran terrorists couldn't have attacked the Federation colony. Their ships only have impulse power, not the warp drive used by the attackers when they escaped. A plot involving Cardassian complicity is revealed. The plan backfires so badly it is obvious their days as the rulers of Bajor are numbered.

THE TORTURE MEISTER

The next appearance of the Cardassians firmly establishes them as a menace greater than the Klingons ever were. In the original STAR TREK, the Klingons were portrayed trying to interfere with a planet's development or to take control of neutral real estate. Battles were rarely on a personal level.

In the two-part NEXT GENERATION episode "Chain Of Command," the Cardassians were given personalities and a sense of menace that lingered long after the encounter. The story appeared shortly before the premiere of DEEP SPACE NINE and clearly established the Cardassians. After this story, everyone would hate the Cardassians without reservation.

Part one of "Chain Of Command" was written by Ronald D. Moore from a story by Frank Abatemarco. Part two is written entirely by Frank Abatemarco. In this story, Captain Picard, along with Worf and Dr. Crusher, go on a secret mission to investigate reports that the Cardassians are using an obscure planet, Celtris III, to develop metagenic weapons. Meanwhile Captain Jellico takes over the Enterprise to negotiate with the Cardassians.

The Cardassians have lured Picard into a trap. One Cardassian, Gul Madred, is unforgettable. Played by David Warner at his most menacing, Gul Madred tortures Picard for information.

They hope to learn the Federation defensive measures for a disputed border zone they want to attack at Minos Kova. This, too, is something of a blind. The Cardassians realize plans would have been changed after Picard's capture. The Cardassians announced the capture to show up Starfleet while protesting this invasion of their sovereignty.

CONTROL THROUGH PAIN

Meanwhile Jean-Luc is hung by his wrists from a crossbar and tortured. When he's unconscious from pain, a device is implanted in his chest inflicts more pain at the press of a button. Gul Madred enjoys himself, completely unmoved by Picard's displays of agony.

The torturer seeks domination through pain. He tries to achieve control of Picard by asking him how many lights he sees on a light bar. There are four lights. When Picard says four the pain is inflicted. Gul Madred wants Picard to say there are five, but Picard refuses.

In a contest of wills, Gul Madred tells Picard he can end his pain by saying what he instructs. He says he doesn't need the battle plans for Minos Kova as one of Picard's comrades has already been tortured into revealing it. Picard refuses to give in as a matter of pride; Gul Madred won't give up out of pride.

The Cardassians symbolize the torturer. It is not a character trait unique to them. Many nations routinely employ torture in the 20th Century, as illustrated in Amnesty International reports.

Patrick Stewart consulted Amnesty International to learn how people act under torture to add realism to his performance. Even as the torture scenes reveal the nature of this Cardassian, the viewer realizes humans and Cardassians have much in common. Members of each race are capable of inflicting pain for power.

One scene reveals common threads between human and alien. Gul Madred's daughter enters his office to briefly speak to her father. Picard questions what kind of world his captor wants his daughter to grow up in and what kind of person she'll turn out to be after being exposed to her father's torturing of prisoners. Gul Madred seems perturbed, proving there's more to him than just a heartless torturer.

ENTER GUL DUKAT

This softer side of Cardassians is seldom revealed. It emerged later when the characters were explored in greater detail on DEEP SPACE NINE.

The premiere episode of DEEP SPACE NINE, titled "Emissary," introduces the Cardassians as an ongoing problem. Marc Alaimo returned as Gul Dukat, the former Cardassian administrator of Deep Space Nine.

He had left reluctantly when Cardassia ordered the abandonment of holdings on Bajor. Gul Dukat opposed this move. He is clearly eager to resume his former position of domination on the space station. The position is now occupied by Commander Ben Sisko of the United Federation of Planets.

Gul Dukat appears to be a grasping bureaucrat who sees a chance for the Cardassians to move back onto Bajor when the wormhole is discovered. Although the Cardassians are blocked, Gul Dukat is not ready to turn his back on Bajor.

A flotilla of Cardassian warships readies to attack Deep Space Nine because it is believed Gul Dukat has met with foul play. When Gul Dukat returns unharmed, the Cardassians are disappointed. They didn't care about their fellow officer as much as they wanted a fight.

THE BUTCHER OF GALLITEPP

In "Emissary" the Cardassians emerge as important players on DEEP SPACE NINE. Just as the Klingons were constantly underfoot on Classic Trek, the Cardassians appear repeatedly on DEEP SPACE NINE. Even in episodes in which they don't appear, they are mentioned.

In "Past Prologue," the second episode of DEEP SPACE NINE, the Cardassians turn up at the space station chasing a former Bajoran terrorist. Garek, the only Cardassian still living on the space station, is introduced. His status as a spy remains open to question. Late in the second season, it is revealed that Garek is an exile from Cardassia who holds grudges against former Cardassian military leaders who ran Deep Space Nine.

One episode turned things on their head. "Duet" offered a tale unlike anything on Classic Trek.

In the original STAR TREK, the Klingons were villains. Only in NEXT

GENERATION were they granted full characterization.

Until episode #18 of DEEP SPACE NINE, the Cardassians were mere villains. Then something startling happened: a Cardassian was shown to possess a conscience.

Written by Peter Allan Fields from a story by Lisa Rich & Jeanne Carrigan-Fauci, "Duet" introduced Aamin Marritza (marvelously played by Harris Yulin) as a former file clerk at the notorious Gallitepp forced labor camp. The episode also revealed Gul Darhe'el, the commandant of Gallitepp, known to the Bajorans as the Butcher of Gallitepp.

CARDASSIAN WAR CRIMES

Aamin Marritza is unlike any other Cardassian. He possesses deep compassion and convictions. At Gallitepp, he suffered every night as he listened to the screams of the tortured and the dying. He hated that Cardassia never faced the consequences of its crimes, and actually denied them.

Aamin Marritza took it upon himself to undergo cosmetic surgery to look like Gul Darhe'el. He then visited the space station where he knew he would be recognized and arrested. By pretending to be himself he could at first protest his innocence, then admit the "truth."

Gul Darhe'el (Aamin Marritza) would then be put on trial for war crimes on Bajor. This would force Cardassia to face the truth of its past atrocities.

When Cardassia learns a citizen is under arrest on Deep Space Nine, Gul Dukat insists he be released and returned home, then refuses to discuss the issue further. This makes Aamin Marritza seem more guilty since Gul Dukat refuses to divulge anything about the prisoner's background.

A background reveals a photo of Gul Darhe'el, who looks exactly like their prisoner. Major Kira and the Bajoran government are ready to convene a war crimes tribunal.

When she confronts Aamin Marritza, he "confesses" and eloquently defends himself. He says that no matter what they do to him now, the dead will remain dead. Confrontations between Marritza and Kira offer powerful performances as each expresses a volatile point of view.

Marritza portrays the perfect unapologetic Cardassian oppressor. He claims he acted to protect Cardassia and that the Bajorans will always be a conquered people.

BAJORAN VENGEANCE

The Bajoran trial will rivet the quadrant's attention on this tiny world and its heritage of torture and brutality under Cardassian domination. Then Odo contacts his former boss, Gul Dukat, and learns that Gul Darhe'el died five years before. Even Gul Dukat is confused by Marritza's claim.

Confronted with the truth, Marritza insists he is the Butcher of Gallitepp. He finally confesses, revealing his desire to make amends for his own cowardice and the crimes of his people. If he's not the Butcher of Gallitepp, he cannot be tried for the crimes of Gul Darhe'el.

Aamin Marritza emerges as a fully realized character, something not before seen in the portrayal of a Cardassian. While Gul Madred in "Chain Of Command" was shown to have some depth, the nonbrutal side of the Cardassian quickly disappeared as he inflicted more pain on Picard. Aamin Marritza wants to recapture his lost soul and end

the screams of the dying he was too cowardly to help.

The actions of Aamin Marritza form a turning point in the portrayal of Cardassians. They aren't all cast from the same mold. Just as Major Kira adjusts her perception of Cardassians, Aamin Marritza is brutally slain by a Bajoran, one of the survivors of Gallitepp.

MORE CARDASSIAN COUNTER PLOTS

This tragic act reveals the depths of hatred the Bajorans hold for their former slavemasters. The death camp survivor regards all Cardassians with equal contempt and considers killing one an act of revenge against the entire race.

Aamin Marritza's description of life at Gallitepp revealed how horrible it was for the Bajorans. His compassion showed there is a previ-

ously unseen side to this race, which made an event in a second season episode more believable.

Harris Yulin's performance as Aamin Marritza was worthy of an Emmy nomination, but STAR TREK never receives Emmy nominations for acting. After all, why should the nominating committee consider a science fiction show as possessing good acting?

The Cardassians made their next significant appearance on DEEP SPACE NINE in the second season premiere in a three-part storyline that began with "The Homecoming." Quark discovers a Bajoran war hero named Li Nalas, believed killed years before. He has been languishing in a secret Cardassian prison camp for ten years.

Major Kira rescues him after a violent engagement with the prison guards. Gul Dukat immediately contacts Commander

Sisko, expresses surprise over the existence of this prison camp and immediately repatriates the rest of the prisoners back to Bajor.

Despite the events of "Duet," that kind of compassion is uncharacteristic of Gul Dukat. Dukat represents the worst of the Cardassians.

REMNANTS OF WAR

It doesn't take long to discover his actions are part of a Cardassian conspiracy. They hope to undermine the Bajoran government by manipulating a political splinter group that wants the Federation off Bajor.

While the Cardassians remain off-screen for almost the entire adventure, their presence powers the story. The splinter group obtained their weapons from the Cardassians, reviving the specter of Bajor returning to Cardassian subjugation. Everyone redoubles their efforts to expose the cul-prits and unravel the conspiracy.

People who otherwise dislike each other put their differences aside rather than face life under the Cardassians again. Cardassia looms large over those who have crossed that world's path of conquest.

The Cardassian legacy continues to effect the running of Bajor. Cardassian war orphans appear in the episode aptly titled "Cardassians." Written by James Crocker from a story by Gene Wolande and John Wright, the tale opens when Deep Space Nine's only resident Cardassian, Garak, meets a Cardassian child on the Promenade.

The boy has been raised by a Bajoran family. When Garak attempts to talk to the boy in a friendly manner, the youth viciously attacks him by biting Garak's hand.

Garak's official connection to Cardassia is questioned when Commander Sisko is contacted by Gul Dukat to inquire about the incident. Dukat uses the incident as evidence Cardassian war orphans are being mistreated by the Bajorans raising them.

The orphans have no status in Cardassian society. They were abandoned on Bajor when the Cardassians returned to their home world.

The storyline exposes Cardassian political intrigues, life on Bajor under the Cardassians, the final days of the civil war and the social rules governing Cardassian family life. The episode reveals more about Cardassian culture than did all previous storylines combined.

A LEGACY OF HATE

Gul Dukat is the catalyst, shaping events from the center of a web of political intrigue. Questions of whether Bajorans are teaching Cardassian war orphans to hate all Cardassians are raised. The boy, Rugal, who brought all this to a head, becomes the focal point of the investigation.

The mysterious Garak spearheads the investigation from behind the scenes by unofficially helping Dr. Bashir search old records at the orphanage. Bashir thinks this will force the Cardassians to deal with the war orphans. Garak points out that the Cardassians don't do anything this major by accident.

Garak and Dr. Bashir cross-reference information about Rugal, including who adopted him and how he came to be at the orphanage. That a Cardassian brought Rugal to the orphanage helps unlock a chain of circumstance pointing directly to Gul Dukat.

Gul Dukat had suggested that DNA samples from Rugal be used to check for living relatives on Cardassia. When Dukat expresses regret his people left the orphans behind, this does not ring true. It was always known the children were there and Gul Dukat expressed no previous concern.

That the Cardassian boy, Rugal, has been raised like a Bajoran is evident when he states that he hates the Cardassians for killing 10 million people during the occupation of Bajor. This not-so-subtly compares the Cardassians to the Nazis of Earth who killed 12 million in their death camps.

The Cardassians often acted like Nazi Stormtroopers. The parallel is easily drawn.

THE WEB OF GUL DUKAT

The web woven by Gul Dukat tightens around a Cardassian politician named Kotan Pedar, an old enemy of Gul Dukat. When the DNA test reveals Rugal is this man's long lost son, previously believed killed by a Bajoran terrorist bomb, pieces fall into place.

If it becomes known on Cardassia that Kotan Pedar abandoned his son on Bajor, he'll be disgraced. While orphans have no status on Cardassia, families are considered vitally important.

What's worse, Rugal has been raised by Bajorans, an inferior race by Cardassian standards. Questions would arise as to why he believed his son killed and how well he tried to search for the boy.

A hearing is held on Deep Space Nine regarding custody of Rugal. The boy doesn't want to go to Cardassia.

Gul Dukat arouses suspicions by appearing in person to witness the proceedings. Why should the former Prefect of Bajor be so interested?

During the inquiry, it is revealed it was a Cardassian military officer who left Rugal at the orphanage; all the other children had been found and brought there by Bajorans. Although this happened seven years before, it appears the boy was separated from his family deliberately to one day humiliate Kotan Pedar. The commanding officer of the Cardassian who brought Rugal to the orphanage was Gul Dukat, who is upset that this accusation is being made.

Rugal is returned to his father and Gul Dukat doesn't make an issue of it as he would surely be brought down. This reveals just one more ruthless incident in the life of this military officer.

WHEN DUKAT RULED

The pivotal episode "Necessary Evil," written by Peter Allan Fields reveals much about Dukat's days as ruler. Life for the Bajorans under the Cardassians is revealed first hand for the first time.

Under Cardassian control, Deep Space Nine was not the bright hub of activity it is now. It is a darker place. There is a furtiveness to everyone's movements that infects the atmosphere with a sense of dread.

As the Prefect of Bajor, Dukat is clearly a man reveling in power, wearing arrogance and a sense of superiority like a badge. Cardassians depend on collaborators to spy on their fellow Bajorans and reveal the names of terrorists. In return, their businesses are protected and they are paid for their services.

It's clear that despite their arrogance, Cardassians fear a mass insurrection. When a collaborator is murdered, Gul Dukat talks Odo into acting as an investigator and a security officer rather than intimidating the Bajorans with strong-arm tactics.

Gul Dukat has Odo investigate because it would be unwise for Cardassians to show concern over the murder of a Bajoran. That could compromise their network of informants.

Gul Dukat points out that the usual response would be to execute five randomly selected Bajorans as an object lesson. Clearly Cardassians regard Bajorans as an inferior race, possibly because they were conquered so easily.

IMMINENT THREATS

Cardassian brutality hangs in the air as an unspoken promise. When Gul Dukat enters during Odo's interrogation of Kira, she knows the Cardassian could execute her on the spot. The Cardassians don't bother with protracted legal proceedings involving mere Bajorans. They kill the suspects and move on to more important matters.

"Necessary Evil" shows why Bajorans despise Cardassians. On post-Cardassian Bajor, Bajorans have little interest in being diplomatic with their former tormentors. After all, the Cardassians displayed no diplomacy dealing with the conquered Bajor.

Cardassians are warlike; their military rules govern society. "The Wounded" revealed their policy finally brought them into direct, armed conflict with the Federation, ending with a peace accord. While there are diplomatic relations between Cardassia and the Federation, they are more formal than cordial.

When Gul Dukat acts cordial it is so exaggerated it is clear he is mocking the Federation. Cardassians look down on the Federation just as they do on Bajorans because the Federation uses the military as a structure, not a design for conquest.

A MILITARISTIC SOCIETY

It would not be exaggeration to compare Cardassians with Romulans. Both are militaristic societies who believe in taking what they want. They both resent the Federation opposing their actions.

The Cardassians reject criticisms of their past actions and proclaim that accusations of war crimes on Bajor are fabricated. That there are Bajoran survivors rendered mute by Cardassian torture leaves them unmoved. To them Bajorans are an inferior race unworthy of compassion.

Aamin Marritza proved some do feel compassion, but how widespread is such anti-military feeling on Cardassia? Life on Cardassia was peaceful until a coalition of military leaders seized power. Once they took over, all activity on the world was directed towards expansion to other planets and domination of other societies.

As long as their actions did not involve worlds aligned with the Federation, the Prime Directive prohibited direct involvement. Then the military leaders of Cardassia became arrogant with their successes and crossed the line, attacking Federation planets.

This led to war and atrocities against Federation outposts. While the war ended in a treaty, Federation suspicion of Cardassia remains. Some events have strained relations such as when the Cardassians attacked a Federation outpost and tried to pin the blame on Bajoran terrorists.

Ultimately the Cardassians decided Bajorans were too much trouble.

THE ANTI-MILITARY UNDERGROUND

The military rulers of Cardassia elevated the lifestyle of the average person. Hunger is now unknown on the home world. That this was accomplished by plundering other worlds and causing starvation on conquered planets doesn't bother Cardassian society.

Not everyone is pleased with life under the military coalition. An anti-military underground movement has gained strength. It remains underground because dissent is not tolerated. Authorities execute known members of the underground.

The Cardassian military has several ranks. Gul indicates a high-ranking officer. Their subordinates have the title Glin. "Guls" are most often dealt with by the Federation. This is followed by the Cardassian Guard, separated into divisions known as "orders." Each "order" consists of three starships.

Cardassia maintains alliances outside the influence of the Federation, such as with Klaestron. As a result, Bajor won't deal with Klaestron, or with the Valerians, who helped the Cardassians by supplying weapons-grade dolamide during the occupation of Bajor.

Other spheres of influence include the world of Kora II where the Cardassians have a military academy. Aamin Marritza was a clerk at the Cardassian military academy on Kora II after he left his assignment at Gallitepp on Bajor.

AN UNEASY TRUCE

Despite Bajor's active opposition to Cardassia, their alliance with the Federation prevents them from blocking Cardassian access to the wormhole. This contributed to unrest when a Bajoran splinter group almost succeeded in having Bajor break all ties with the Federation.

Cardassia would have loved that. They've been wanting to regain control of Bajor ever since the wormhole was discovered.

The wormhole is in a region of space previously considered unsafe for starship navigation. It was only after the Cardassians left Bajor that the wormhole was discovered.

Heads must have rolled on Cardassia. The race had dominated another world for fifty years without discovering the doorway. It remains unknown how long the wormhole has existed since, being artificial, at some point it was completed and activated.

Cardassians know it is controlled by a coalition of Bajor and the Federation. It is unlikely the Cardassians will stop trying to get it back. They've already been at war with the Federation. This is why they attempt to secure it through subterfuge, a course less costly than intergalactic warfare.

Cardassians loom large in the STAR TREK universe of the 24th Century, appearing on key episodes of both NEXT GENERATION and DEEP SPACE NINE. They exert their greatest influence in the latter.

Had there never been a DEEP SPACE NINE then the Bajorans would have remained peripheral figures on STAR TREK—THE NEXT GENERATION. Since DS9 began, Bajor has been explored in ways THE NEXT GENERATION reserved only for Klingons and Romulans.

BAJOR: WORLD ON THE EDGE

Viewers didn't know it at the time, but when the fifth season episode "Ensign Ro" introduced the aliens known as Bajorans, it was the first appearance of characters who would become vital to the STAR TREK universe a little more than a year later.

"Ensign Ro," written by Michael Piller from a story by Rick Berman and Michael Piller, introduced the Bajorans as both refugees and terrorists. Ensign Ro Laren appeared as a Starfleet officer court marshaled for disobeying orders costing away team members their lives.

Starfleet transferred her to the Enterprise as an expert on Bajoran affairs when the ship tracks down a Bajoran terrorist. She is no happier on the ship than the bridge officers are to see her.

Ro Laren is a tour guide to the Bajoran people and their history. When the Enterprise arrives at Valo III, Ensign Ro is part of the away team sent down to the Bajoran refugee camp.

Although they search for a terrorist named Orta, the visit to Valo III presents an opportunity to explain the Bajorans. Ensign Ro relates the history of the Cardassian oppression of Bajor and why Orta fights.

The refugee camp is very poor because other worlds don't wish to accept Bajoran refugees that might offend the Cardassians. A tour of the Bajoran people shows why Ro Laren is bitter. She recounts watching the Cardassians murder her father when she was a child.

This quickly establishes a backstory for the Bajorans, something uncommon for NEXT GENERATION. Ordinarily aliens are defined only by the problems facing their world and seldom given personalities or histories. Extra effort was taken with the Bajorans, an early clue that

Michael Piller had something special in mind.

ENTER DEEP SPACE NINE

Gene Roddenberry died shortly after the original airing of "Ensign Ro." Plans then crystallized for the final development of DEEP SPACE NINE.

Berman and Piller originally wanted to use the Ensign Ro character in the new series, but actress Michelle Forbes turned down the offer. Instead an entirely new Bajoran character, Major Kira, was created.

Major Kira hates Cardassians, although less has been revealed about her some 40 episodes into DEEP SPACE NINE than was told of Ensign Ro in one story. Kira Nerys was involved in a Bajoran underground killing on the Cardassian space station. Major Kira's story begins when she became part of the Ops team aboard Deep Space Nine.

Before the Cardassians left Deep Space Nine and Bajor, the Federation took a neutral stance on the occupation. The Bajorans resent this.

Neutrality has loopholes. If a Federation world sells arms to an unaligned world that world can still deal with Bajor or Cardassia. It can make a mockery of the neutrality.

HISTORY LESSONS

"Ensign Ro" is a turning point for the Federation on the Bajoran issue. The Federation discovers that the Cardassians attacked a Federation colony and blamed it on Bajoran terrorists. The Cardassians find that the Federation no longer looks kindly on them.

The Bajorans were not explored beyond that one episode. While Ensign Ro remained on board the Enterprise throughout the remainder of the fifth season, her Bajoran background was never again an issue in the stories.

The background of Bajor is contradictory. The series Writer's Guide stipulates that the Cardassians were on Bajor for a hundred years, but in actual aired stories the references have ranged from 40 to 60 years. Although Bajor is now a poor world due to abuse by the Cardassians, it is still a beautiful world rich in a deeply religious culture.

Before the invasion by the Cardassians, Bajor was an independent, self-sustaining planet uninterested in joining the Federation. The Bajorans couldn't imagine anyone would try to subjugate them.

Bajor is the largest world in its planetary system. It is the only one with an indigenous population. Five moons orbit Bajor; the fifth is called Jeraddo. This moon became the site of Bajor's first large-scale energy project tapping the moon's molten core. There was a controversy when 50 inhabitants of the moon had to be relocated, some of them forcibly.

DISCOVERING THE WORMHOLE

During the 22nd Century, a Bajoran leader named Kai Taluno was in the Denorios Belt not far from Bajor when his spacecraft malfunctioned. While trying to get it fixed, he experienced what he believed to be a vision of "the heavens opening up." In the 24th century this vision came to mind when the wormhole was discovered in the Denorios Belt.

The wormhole has become integral to the commerce of Bajor and an important element of DEEP SPACE NINE. The wormhole supposedly remained undiscovered because the Denorios Asteroid Belt contains a charged plasma field that interferes with spacecraft, not unlike the problems Kai Taluno experienced.

The Denorios Asteroid Belt is the source of the strange orbs called the Tears of the Prophets. Nine such orbs have been discovered, although all but one ultimately fell into the hands of the Cardassians. A group of Bajoran monks specializes in the study of the Orbs and is aware of their ability to cause visions of the future in some.

One of the Orbs figured in the first DEEP SPACE NINE episode, "The Emissary," and in the first three episodes of season two when Major Kira experienced a vision after touching one.

The Bajoran wormhole, unlike other wormholes discovered in the Alpha Quadrant, is completely stable. There was a Barzan wormhole that once appeared stable but eventually opened into the Gamma Quadrant and shifted position over time.

The Bajoran Wormhole is unique in that it is artificial, constructed by a race of beings the Bajorans call "The Prophets." Whether they are the gods of Bajoran religion isn't established, but Bajorans don't doubt their identity.

REFUGEES FROM THE WORMHOLE

The Bajoran Wormhole opens into the Gamma Quadrant, but its other end never drifts out of its established coordinates. The point in the Gamma Quadrant the wormhole opens to is 70 thousand light-years beyond Starbase 85, the furthest established outpost of the Federation in the Alpha Quadrant.

The Gamma Quadrant was not opened to the Federation until the premiere of DEEP SPACE NINE. Very little is established about the planets in that quadrant of space.

Alien beings and worlds of DEEP SPACE NINE are only explored for a single episode, with the exceptions of Bajor and the Cardassians. The Gamma Quadrant remains a realm of mystery. Visitors from the Gamma Quadrant arrive on Deep Space Nine, do good or ill, then return home.

An exception when Bajor became involved with people from the Gamma Quadrant was chronicled in "Sanctuary." The story told of three million refugees searching for a home.

To Bajor, accepting a sudden, massive influx of refugees was out of the question. Bajor is not xenophobic, but the economy is recovering from brutal exploitation by the Cardassians.

The Scrian refugees are the first aliens from the Gamma Quadrant revealed as individuals with a background. They have been searching for a legendary planet known to them as Kintana.

They were slaves on their own world until it was invaded and conquered by a race known as the Dominion. The Scrians then fled their former slave masters.

THE KINTANA QUESTION

This is not the only time the Dominion has been mentioned in DEEP SPACE NINE, nor is it the first. "Rules Of Acquisition" offered mention of the Dominion when Quark entered the Gamma Quadrant to establish trade routes for the Ferengi. Whether they are friend or foe to the Federation is not established.

The Scrians are a matriarchy because male Scrians constantly fight. This is more than we know about other cultures from the Gamma Quadrant.

Major Kira makes friends with Haneek, one of the first Scrians to pass through the wormhole to Deep Space Nine. When Haneek insists her study of Bajor reveals it is Kintana, Major Kira holds out cautious hope and says the provisional government of Bajor will discuss the possibility.

Bajor turns the offer down, much to the consternation of the Scrians. This creates a dangerous confrontation.

Some male Scrians try to take a shuttle to the surface and fire on a Bajoran patrol ship, which is forced to defend itself and destroy the Scrian shuttle. The Scrians are so disheartened they withdraw their plea to settle on Bajor.

This incident further established the precarious position of Bajoran society, despite the increased commerce brought to the sector because of the worm hole.

BAJORAN DETAILS

Just as the Enterprise is the focal point for stories on NEXT GENERATION, the space station and Bajor center the action of DEEP SPACE NINE. Even when a story takes place entirely on Deep Space Nine, events are influenced by Bajor or the Bajoran people.

Bajor is in no position to launch explorations through the wormhole. Its own spacecraft only have impulse power with no warp capability. The limited development of space flight technology left Bajor open to invasion by the Cardassians.

Whenever a Bajoran dignitary wants to go through the wormhole, they go to Deep Space Nine and ask Commander Sisko for help. Kai Opaka took such a flight in "Battle Lines."

Cultural heritage is very important to Bajorans, as exemplified by their annual Gratitude Festival. This was once a religious celebration honoring the Prophets, but is now a festival celebrating independence from Cardassia.

Once the Cardassians left Bajor, the puppet Bajoran Provisional Government expanded to include all political positions. Ministers alone have voting rights, with Kaval being the Minister of State. The Bajoran legal system includes a personage known as the Arbiter, an individual who acts as a legal judge.

FACETS OF BAJORAN CULTURE

Bajor is rich in scenic wonders. These include the Fire Caverns, a natural wonder that survived the Cardassian occupation.

Bajor is still recovering from destruction and artisans and musicians have nowhere to perform. The physical needs of the

Bajorans have been given precedence over their culture. Wandering minstrels and musicians perform to practice their skills and earn a meager income from their craft.

Bajoran musical compositions known as Serenas run the full gamut from dark and soulful to bright and exuberant.

In the 24th Century, the Bajorans achieved their independence from Cardassia but still search for self-esteem. The Dal'Rok is a mythical creature conjured by a village storyteller called the Sirah. It helps unite the village, forcing people to put aside their differences to drive off the strange being.

The Dal'Rok is created by the Sirah by means of a shard of one of the "Tears of the Prophets." Once a year the Sirah unites the villagers to drive off the Dal'Rok reaffirming their belief in themselves.

A MONUMENT TO THE PAST

The Bajorans preserve symbols of their oppression so new generations will remember what happens when a people become complacent. One symbol is Gallitepp, a forced labor camp run by the Cardassians under the command of Gul Darhe'el, whom history has dubbed "the Butcher Of Gallitepp."

Gul Darhe'el has become the embodiment of Cardassian oppression. The survivors of Gallitepp have become the symbol of survival in the face of awful adversity.

More has been revealed about the Bajorans than any other race presented on STAR TREK, with the possible exceptions of the Klingons and the Romulans. Emerging from background characters in "Ensign Ro," the Bajorans became vital elements of STAR TREK in the 24th Century.

DEEP SPACE NINE deals more with religion than did THE NEXT GENERATION. Two religions are regularly portrayed. The first is the Bajoran faith, the other that of the Ferengi.

RELIGIOUS BELIEFS
IN DEEP SPACE NINE
A COMPARATIVE STUDY

by Diane K. McCarty

The Bajoran people are highly religious. During the Cardassian occupation of Bajor, the spiritual unity of its people saved the oppressed race. The leader of the Bajoran church, the Kai Opaka, kept the people together.

Major Kira Nerys told Commander Benjamin Sisko, "Our religion is the only thing that holds my people together. If [Opaka] would call for unity, they'd listen." Soon afterward the commander met the Kai while she lived in seclusion in a Bajoran monastery.

The Bajorans believe, as Kai Opaka told Sisko, "A Bajoran draws courage from his spiritual life. Our life force, or pagh, is replenished by the Prophets." A Bajoran cleric can "read" a person's pagh by grasping their ear. This has been described as an unpleasant experience by those who have endured it.

Opaka led Sisko down a hidden passageway to an underground, candlelit chamber, the storehouse of a jeweled box in which was housed "The Tear of a Prophet." This spinning, glittery, hourglass-shaped "orb" was sent to Bajor from the legendary "Celestial Temple." Through the orbs, people experience visions of the past and future, and receive knowledge of the Prophets.

Over ten thousand years, nine such orbs appeared in the Bajoran sky. All but one were captured by the Cardassians during the occupation of Bajor.

The Cardassians performed experiments on the orbs to try to unravel their secrets. They failed. No handful of infidel Cardassian scientists could hope to accomplish what innumerable holy members of the Bajoran religious orders—fully steeped in the lore of their religion—could not accomplish over a period

of thousands and thousands of years.

Kai Opaka's greatest fear was that the Cardassians would locate and destroy the Celestial Temple. She gave Sisko the last remaining orb, entrusting him to find the temple. Fortunately, he succeeded.

BAJORAN CATHOLICS?

Not much is understood about the Prophets. The only person with face-to-face contact is Sisko, whom the Bajorans dubbed "The Emissary." The Prophets have no concept of linear time. They manifested themselves to Sisko as people he had known in his life. Their true appearance is unknown.

The Prophets see past, present and future as the same; what has happened is forever a part of that person's existence. They do not believe what is past is now gone forever. So alien was this concept that

they first thought Sisko was lying about it.

Physical pleasure is unknown to them. The Prophets may be non-corporeal beings. They live inside the wormhole, on what appears to be a planet. The world appears to be dark and rocky with an eternal, rainless, thunderstorm flashing above. It is also believed the Prophets created the wormhole.

The Bajoran religion is comparable in structure to the Roman Catholic Church on Earth. The Kai is a direct counterpart of the Pope, the spiritual and pastoral leader. Just as the Catholic Church has cardinals, the Bajoran church has the Vedek Assembly. The religious communities of both churches are divided into orders. Some orders are more conservative than others.

RELIGIOUS PARALLELS

Similarities extend to the trappings of the two religions. Both churches use candles and incense in their ceremonies. Members wear robes and vestments that make up the habits indicative of their vocation. They often live in cloistered monasteries and worship in chapels.

Bajoran monks sing long, continuous chants, not unlike Catholic Gregorian chants. Both faiths believe in the existence of a Devil, the supreme embodiment of Evil. The Bajorans revere and worship the Prophets, praying to them and receiving spiritual instruction from them; Catholics worship God in the same way. An integral belief of both religions is that their deity, or deities, teach them patience.

Unlike the Catholic religious hierarchy, Bajoran clerics are not required to take oaths of celibacy. Their women do not marry the Prophets, as nuns "marry" Christ, and the men do not marry the Church, as do Catholic priests. They are free to marry among their people.

In the Bajoran religion, no distinction is made between male and female clerics. Men and women are equally eligible to become a Vedek or even the Kai. Both sexes are free to preach before the assembled Bajoran people. In the Catholic Church, only men can become priests, bishops, cardinals or popes, and only men can perform the religious ceremonies such as Mass and the administration of the Holy Sacraments.

Some Bajorans seem fanatical in their devotion to their spiritual philosophies. Vedek Winn, the leader of a small, right-wing order, accused the human teacher Keiko O'Brien of leading Bajoran school children into blasphemy by not telling them about the Prophets' connection to the wormhole. Although it is unproved, there is speculation that Winn was involved with a failed assassination attempt upon Vedek Bariel, a charismatic and far more liberal religious leader, who is next in line to become the new Kai.

One last similarity exists between the religions of Earth and Bajor: political maneuvering and bloodthirsty "devotion" to close-minded ideology. Earth has manifested this in The Inquisition, the Crusades, jihads (or "holy wars") and other persecutions. Bajor, too, has had its share of atrocities.

FERENGI DEVOTION

Other ideologies exist among the races of DEEP SPACE NINE. Although not formally recognized as a religion, the Ferengi have a unique formal system of beliefs. While the Bajorans worship the Prophets, the Ferengi worship The Profits. Their religious dogma is composed solely of the sacred Rules of Acquisition, all 285 of them, plus accompanying commentaries.

Following are some of the most important Rules:

#1: Once you have their money, never give it back.

#6: Never allow family to stand in the way of opportunity.

#7: Keep your ears open.

#16: A deal is a deal.

#21: Never place friendship above profit.

#22: The Wise can hear profit in the wind.

#31: Never make fun of a Ferengi's mother.

#33: It never hurts to suck up to the boss.

#47: Don't trust a man wearing a better suit than your own.

#48: The bigger the smile, the sharper the knife.

#57: Good customers are as rare as latinum. Treasure them.

#59: Free advice is seldom cheap.

#62: The riskier the road, the quicker the profit.

#76: Every once in a while declare peace. It confuses the hell out of your enemies.

#109: Dignity and an empty sack is worth a sack.

#112: Never have sex with the boss' sister.

#139: Wives or brothers inherit.

#194: It's always good business to know about customers before they walk in your door.

HEAVEN AND HELL: FERENGI STYLE

To Ferengi, all that glitters is gold (gold press latinum, that is). Of all Earth songs, the Ferengi favorite is "Stairway to Heaven" by Twentieth Century rock ensemble Led Zeppelin. They especially savor the first line: "There's a lady who's sure/All that Glitters is gold. And she's buying a stairway to Heaven."

Young Ferengi boys are expected to memorize all Rules and their commentaries. Later, they are expected to abide by the rules. Ferengi education is a matter of sink or swim. They mercilessly throw their young into the cutthroat world of commerce to see if they thrive.

Despite the apparent respect most Ferengi feel for their mother, as shown in Rule #31, their society is misogynist. Ferengi women "stay in their place," barefoot (or totally bare) and pregnant, in the kitchen. They do not seek the "nobler" pursuits of Ferengi life.

It is against the law to accept financial advice from a Ferengi female, just as it is against the law for the women to wear clothing. This philosophy flourishes even though Ferengi women are as intelligent as Ferengi men, and just as capable of pursuing profitable ventures.

The Ferengi believe in Hell, a place of eternal poverty. Heaven is achieved by walking up the Latinum Stairway.

THE LOBES HAVE IT

Ferengi swear by their rather well-endowed ear lobes. A Ferengi's ability to raise profits is measured by the size of his lobes. The unfortunate Ferengi male born with small lobes is frequently the object of scorn and ridicule.

To the Ferengi, the Almighty Profit is more important than family, friends or even life itself. Ferengi do not bury their dead; they vacuum desiccate the corpse and package it as relics. The relics are sold by the dead Ferengi's family so that, even in death, a Ferengi can still make a profit.

Many may consider the Ferengi "religious" philosophies misguided, but none dispute their devotion. Bajoran and Ferengi beliefs clash when the two races meet in close quarters at a place called Deep Space Nine.

In the STAR TREK of the 24th Century, Klingons are very different than in the 23rd Century version of STAR TREK.

KLINGONS IN THE 24TH CENTURY

In the 23rd Century, Klingons wore black hats; they were one-note bad guys trotted out whenever a nasty troublemaker was needed. The tradition continued in the movies, particularly STAR TREK III: THE SEARCH FOR SPOCK and STAR TREK VI: THE UNDISCOVERED COUNTRY. STAR TREK VI, the turning point in the portrayal of Klingons, still shows evil, warlike Klingons. It was as if they needed one last chance for an evil Klingon to battle Kirk and Spock.

The 24th Century Klingon Empire is an active part of the Federation. Klingons have not been domesticated.

Now that the Klingons are allies of the Federation, they grow and change as characters. They have become far more interesting than in the original STAR TREK.

Worf's presence on the starship Enterprise may denote initial tokenism. Late in the first season of NEXT GENERATION, in the episode "Heart Of Glory," the story centered on Worf and other Klingons. The episode changed everything; Klingons on STAR TREK would never be the same again.

BUILDING A BETTER KLINGON

The portrayal of Klingon culture in the 24th Century STAR TREK universe usually involves Worf, the most visible representative. One Klingon-oriented episode of THE NEXT GENERATION didn't feature Worf prominently yet revealed a great deal about Klingons. A memorable episode late in the second season of DEEP SPACE NINE was the first appearance of Klingons on that series.

When Gene Roddenberry developed STAR TREK—THE NEXT GENERATION he knew he wanted to elevate the Klingons from their previous thankless role. He was determined to see the

Klingons become interesting characters.

Worf was a gruff but likable crew member in the first season. Not much was revealed about the Klingon people of this era until late in the season. That episode, "Heart Of Glory," was written by Maurice Hurley from a story by Maurice Hurley, Herb Wright and D.C. Fontana.

HEART OF GLORY

In this episode, the Enterprise rescues three Klingons from a disabled ship. One is badly hurt.

While he's treated in sickbay, the others, Kunivas and Koris, test Worf's allegiances. They are suspicious of a Klingon who serves on a Federation ship. Since these are the first Klingons to appear on THE NEXT GENERATION other than Worf, the viewer doesn't know how friendly the average Klingon is towards Starfleet.

Kunivas and Koris bait Worf, not only because he

wears a Federation uniform but because he wasn't raised on Klinzai. They openly wonder if he's a "tame" Klingon.

When the wounded Klingon dies, the others, Worf, Kunivas and Koris, stand over the body and emit the loud, ear-ringing Klingon Death Chant. It is a warning that a Klingon is on his way to the netherworld. This Klingon equivalent of a funereal dirge is a real revelation of how different their ways are from human customs.

"Sto-Vo-Kor" is the Klingon belief in an afterlife, a place they refer to as the netherworld. Their belief is similar to that of ancient Terran Greeks, Vikings and other groups who believe in only one destination after death, be it Hades or Valhalla.

Not all Klingons are pleased with the peace accord between the Federation and the Klingon Empire. The three rescued by the Enterprise grew up in a culture which prizes the craft of the warrior and dying in combat. Yet they no longer have any traditional enemies, and are no longer at war.

The peace treaty was signed some 75 years before. These warriors grew up hearing about "the good old days" when conflict with the Federation was frequent and violent.

DEATH WITH DIGNITY

Kunivas, Koris and their comrade were determined to live a traditional Klingon life. They stole a ship and destroyed the Klingon vessel sent to bring them back, becaming outlaws from their own empire.

They are taken into custody in a revealing scene. When the security team arrives to arrest them, a child accidentally happens on the scene. For a tense moment, it is believed a hostage situation is arising. Kunivas and Koris surrender the child, saying Klingons do not make war on children.

This is far different from the way Klingons were portrayed in the original STAR TREK and the movies. Then Kirk's unarmed son was slain by a Klingon in STAR TREK III: THE SEARCH FOR SPOCK.

This scene in "Heart Of Glory" demonstrates that although the Klingons are outlaws, they uphold codes of honor which guide them into their adult lives. Gene Roddenberry was closely guiding THE NEXT GENERATION at this time, but kept at arms length from creative control of the last several STAR TREK movies.

When Worf appeals to the captain of the approaching Klingon vessel, an aspect of their culture is revealed. Worf asks that Kunivas and Koris be exiled to a hostile world to die as warriors rather than be executed. While the Klingon commander sympathizes, he believes Kunivas and Koris must be confined so they will not violate the Klingon alliance with the Federation.

Then the Klingons escape from their holding cell and kill two guards. Kunivas is killed during the escape.

In their final confrontation, Worf kills Koris to save the Enterprise. As a show of respect, Worf performs the Klingon death ritual, howling a warning as the Klingon dies.

The crew members of the Enterprise look stunned when they witness Worf perform the death chant rituals. It is clearly a very dramatic event, particularly by human standards.

LIFE ON A KLINGON SHIP

The next portrayal of Klingon culture was not an episode centered on Worf. "A Matter Of Honor," written by Burton Armus from a story by Wanda M. Haight, Gregory Amos and Burton Armus, instead focuses on Will Riker. When Riker volunteers to be part of a Starfleet exchange program, he is temporarily transferred to the Klingon starship the Pagh where he serves as First Officer.

Preparing for the experience, Riker eats Klingon food aboard the Enterprise. One dish is "Gakh," the first time this delicacy was portrayed. Gakh looks like a bowl of large, live, squiggling worms. It is supposed to be eaten live. Serving half-dead Gakh is is very bad form.

Riker gets swift lessons in brutal discipline aboard the Pagh. As First Officer he is obliged to kill the captain if the captain is derelict in his duties. The Second Officer is obligated to do the same for him.

The Klingons view Riker as their inferior because he is human, but he quickly demonstrates he can be just as violent and aggressive as a Klingon. He earns their respect.

Klingon women aboard the Pagh display aggressive attentions towards Riker. He finds the women's ribald comments amusing and joins in their laughter. The story portrays two very different cultures displaying their similarities and differences.

CULTURE CLASH

The captain of the Pagh demands the security codes for the Enterprise from Riker. When he refuses, the captain congratulates him for not betraying his captain. Had Riker done so, Captain K'Argan would have executed him for treason. The Pagh is a very dark vessel, unlike the wide, brightly lit rooms and corridors of the Enterprise.

Late in the second season, an episode focused on Worf. It presented the first full characterization of a female Klingon on NEXT GENERATION. In "The Emissary," Suzia Plakson is introduced as K'Ehleyr, a half-Klingon/half-human woman.

K'Ehleyr and Worf had been more than just friends years before. Yet, when she arrives aboard the Enterprise from a scout shuttle, she's strictly business.

This is a crossover with the old version of the Klingons. The Klingon Empire has discovered that an old vessel whose crew has been in cryonic suspension for 75 years.

They are about to awaken the sleeping Klingon crew. K'Ehleyr is supposed to help the Enterprise avert a possible crisis. These Klingons know nothing of an alliance with the Federation and will regard a Federation ship as an enemy.

No Klingon vessel is close enough to intercept them. The Enterprise tries to reach the old Klingon ship so that K'Ehleyr can delay the awakening.

MORE KLINGON RITUALS

Worf and K'Ehleyr show how male and female Klingons act with each other. On the holodeck they engage in a battle simulation which erotically stimulates them both. A sexually aroused Klingon is an unusual sight to see. Worf wants to take the mating vow with K'Ehleyr, but she declines because she doesn't highly value Klingon tradition.

Their "shared past" will emerge again in a later episode when Worf discovers he has a seven year old son he never knew about. Worf and K'Ehleyr make an interesting pair since he was raised by humans while she is half-human, although she appears to be full Klingon.

The resolution to this story is interesting. They arrive at the rendezvous point too late to delay the awakening. Worf and K'Ehleyr make peaceful contact with the old Klingon vessel by convincing them Klingon defeated the Federation and K'Ehleyr and Worf are in command of the starship Enterprise.

While the third season episode "The Bonding" is not a Klingon story, Worf is prominently featured. A private Klingon ritual called the "R'uusta" is revealed.

The episode is written by Ronald Moore. It tells of the death of crew member Marla Astor while on an away team commanded by Lt. Worf. When she is killed, her 12-year-old son Jeremy is orphaned. Worf feels responsible for the boy.

At the conclusion, Worf performs a Klingon bonding ceremony with Jeremy after the boy comes to understand they are both orphans. The touching, private ceremony honors the memory of dead parents and makes them brothers.

"The Bonding" is one of the finest episodes in the seven year run of THE NEXT GENERATION.

KLINGON POLITICS

Klingon culture is put under the microscope in season three's "Sins Of The Father," written by Ronald D. Moore and W. Reed Moran from a story by Drew Deighan. When Worf discovers his long-lost younger brother Kurn lives, it is a bittersweet reunion. The Klingon High Council has declared their deceased father a traitor who collaborated with the Romulans, causing the Khitomer Massacre.

Kurn seeks out Worf because the eldest son must defend the honor of the family before the High Council. Should the charges not be disproven, then the dishonor will be borne by the family for seven generations. Worf may face execution for his father's crime.

A Klingon trial is called a Mek'ba. The accused may have a defender appointed; this defender is called a cha'Dlch.

Worf proves the evidence used to bring the charges against his father is phony. The political intrigues which plague

Klingon government are no less nefarious than that of other worlds.

The High Council didn't know Worf was the son of the man accused. When Kurn is injured as the brothers foil an assassination attempt, Jean-Luc Picard steps in as Worf's "second." They learn Worf's old nurse also survived Khitomer, and search her out to testify before the High Council.

When she appears before the Council, the conspiracy is exposed. The conspirators didn't expect their condemnation of Worf's family to be successfully challenged. The Council meets with Worf behind closed doors and explains that were the name of the real traitor revealed, it would tear the government apart and threaten the power structure of the Empire.

MORE KLINGON POLITICS

For the good of the Empire, Worf agrees to accept discommendation. He is banished from decent society and looked down on by all other Klingons. Worf makes this sacrifice for the good of his planet.

With this action, Worf demonstrates the depth of his loyalty. This doesn't mean he's willing to forget it. Honor is everything to a Klingon. Worf vows to one day regain his family's honor.

First Worf gets something back he didn't know about. This reveals something about Klingon fatherhood in the 24th Century. It happens in the fourth season episode "Reunion," written by Thomas Perry and Jo Perry and Ronald D. Moore and Brandon Braga from a story by Drew Deighan and Thomas Perry and Jo Perry.

Suzie Plakson returns as K'Ehleyr in a story which shows how Klingon leaders are chosen. When K'Mpec, the leader of the High Council, learns he is dying from poison, he turns to Picard as an independent party he can trust to act as an arbitrator.

K'Ehleyr is part of the group accompanying K'Mpec. She now wants to accept the proposal of marriage Worf made in "The Emissary." Because of his discommendation, Worf declines as he doesn't wish to bring dishonor on K'Ehleyr.

Although Worf won't marry K'Ehleyr, she decides it is time to reveal that Worf has a son. This comes as a surprise to him. The boy's name is Alexander. Worf wants to do right by the boy, but doesn't want his own dishonor carried over to the child.

TURNING POINTS

As arbitrator, Picard wants the most archaic form of the ceremony of ascension performed. This requires the challengers for the position of leadership of the High Council to perform a long recitation of accomplishments, a ritual which could take hours or days.

One of the challengers, Duras, realizes K'Ehleyr has discovered he is the traitor and murders her. Worf claims the "Right of Revenge." The Klingons reluctantly agree because K'Ehleyr was Worf's mate.

Worf fights Duras to the death, disposing of the man who brought disgrace on his family name and murdered his mate. Revenge is a very important right in Klingon culture. No one can stand in the way of a warrior who claims this right. Dueling to the death is the most honorable way a Klingon can die.

Although Duras is dead, Worf waits for the right time to regain his family honor. Honor is as important as revenge.

CIVIL WAR

In "Redemption," Worf regains the good name of his family. The two part story by Ronald D. Moore spans the climax of season four and the premiere episode of season five.

The Klingon ascension had resulted in Gowron being named new head of the High Council. Klingon politics are still murky since the death of Duras. His two sisters have gained influence on the High Council and found a young man they claim is their brother's illegitimate son.

Factions have erupted in the council. Instability in the government is leading to a Klingon civil war.

Although Gowron is the officially appointed leader of the High Council, the Federation cannot interfere in civil conflicts on Klinzai. That would violate the Prime Directive. A planet must solve its own internal problems without the interference of other worlds.

The Federation and Klingons eventually discover that the Romulans are behind the attempts to destabilize the Klingon Empire. This puts a new light on things.

Before the Romulan subterfuge is revealed, Worf boards his brother, Kurn's vessel fighting on the side of Gowron. Gowron agrees to restore Worf's family honor.

The Council has already been shattered by the treachery of the Duras sisters. Gowron is not just fighting for his title, but his life, and will accept anyone who will side with him.

Worf's honor is restored in a ceremony in which he grabs a naked sword blade without showing pain. Klingons never show pain.

Klingons claim to value honor. They venerate martial skill and welcome combat.

HONOR REGAINED

When the Federation learns Romulans are behind the Klingon civil war, they agree to sever the Romulan supply line. The Romulans will not be able to interfere with the private disagreements of the Klingons.

When the tide turns, the Duras sisters escape but fall into disgrace and must flee the Klingon Empire. As is his right, Worf is given a chance to slay the pretender to the throne. He refuses, seeing no honor in slaying a child. This dishonors the young man as he cannot die a Klingon but will be imprisoned instead.

The two episodes reveal how Klingons think and act with one another. A scene in a tavern shows Klingons drinking and laughing together even though they serve on opposing ships in the civil conflict. They respect each other as equals and will meet as such in combat.

What it means to be a Klingon is explored in the fifth season episode "Ethics," written by Ronald D. Moore from a story by Sara Charno and Stuart Charno. When Worf's spine is seriously injured in an accident aboard the Enterprise, the prognosis is that he will never walk again without artificial supports.

In Klingon society to be crippled is to be useless. Such citizens commit suicide rather than live as an object of pity.

CRITICAL CHOICES

In a warrior society, life as a cripple has no meaning. It raises the question whether all scientists in Klingon society grow up as warriors cracking skulls when they're not cracking their calculus books. This has not been dealt with by STAR TREK. Even the single-minded Ferengi have been shown to have scientists.

Worf is dispirited by his injuries and contemplates suicide. When Riker refuses to help Worf consummate this terminal ritual, the injured warrior turns to his son, Alexander.

For a time, he had refused to allow his son to see him as a cripple. Worf finally relents and sees Alexander because the boy worries about his father. Worf considers asking his son to help him committ

suicide, but can't bring himself to go through with it.

Instead Worf defies Dr. Crusher and undergoes experimental spine replacement surgery. While the viewer knows Worf will not be killed, the story still delivers a powerful lesson in the differences between human and Klingon culture.

What human society considers an endurable handicap, and even euphmistically calls "physically challenged," Klingon society regards as a reason to stop living. Worf insisted repeatedly that even if he regained eighty percent of his mobility with prosthetics, he would still be an object of pity.

The success of the operation is partially due to the back-up systems in the bodies of Klingons. Their biology is the least discussed part of the race, although slightly more is known about Klingon physiology than Klingon doctors.

The profession was never portrayed in the 28 year history of STAR TREK. Worf's nurse is as close to the Klingon medical profession as has been shown to date.

A FATE WORSE THAN DEATH

Worf suffers a personal crisis in the sixth season episode "Birthright," written by Brannon Braga. Yridian tells Worf his father is captive on a Romulan prison planet. Worf becomes infuriated. For a Klingon to be imprisoned rather than die in combat is a disgrace that extends to the entire family.

Yridian guides Worf to the jungle planet. He is to be picked up again in two days.

Worf discovers that the Romulan prison encampment is peopled by Klingons and their offspring. This outrages Worf, particularly since the Klingons accept their imprisonment with no ill will and have not taught their children their Klingon heritage. Worst of all, the Klingons do not want to be rescued and returned to their homeworld.

The Klingon prisoners reveal that to return home would be to disgrace their families. A Romulan commander watches over the Klingons and treats them well.

The Romulan commander has married a Klingon woman and has a daughter, Ba'el. Worf is scandalized. The concept of a union between a Klingon and a Romulan is unthinkable to the people of his home world.

This episode explores the Klingon concept of honor applied to captives. One of the Klingon men, L'Kor, says that should his son discover him alive, he hopes his son would be Klingon enough to kill him. Being held captive is the ultimate dishonor a Klingon warrior can experience.

LEGENDS COME TO LIFE

Worf realizes how bad things are when he sees a Klingon youth using a ceremonial spear as a gardening tool. The boy clearly doesn't know what it is. When he questions the youth, the boy explains that his parents came to this world to escape the war.

Worf shows the youth what it means to be a Klingon by example. Worf indulges in the "Mok'Bara," a Klingon exercise ritual. This routine helps center the mind and the body and is practiced during times of great stress. Stress is what Worf is feeling.

The younger Klingons finds this new exercise fascinating. The outsider, Worf wins the trust of the young Klingons tells them stories of their heritage, tales their parents chose not to repeat. He tells of

Kahless, the great Klingon warrior who fought and died 1500 years before.

Worf trains the youths in the weapons and implements left lying around, including its history. Each Klingon weapon has a purpose with cultural significance.

The warrior race has a rich cultural tradition spanning thousands of years. On Klinzai, Kahless is virtually a religious icon.

MOMENT OF TRUTH

When Tokath, the Romulan in charge of the village tries to stop Worf from disrupting this tiny Klingon society, Worf refuses. He prefers execution to turning his back on his heritage.

Then the stories and ideals Worf taught the young Klingons bears fruit. One by one they come forward to stand at Worf's side and die alongside him rather than abandon what it means to be Klingon.

Tokath relents and allows Worf to leave with

whoever wants to accompany him. They agree to keep the place secret lest the families of these old warriors be dishonored on Klinzai.

Worf claims the Klingons he's found are crash survivors. It must have been difficult for them to join normal Klingon society on Klinzai. Worf could hardly have taught them all the subtlties in the few days he spent tutoring them.

Ba'el remained on the prison planet. Her Romulan heritage would be unacceptable to other Klingons. Through no fault of her own she has become an outcast, although until Worf's appearance she had been happy in her simple, sheltered life.

A CRISIS OF FAITH

The mention of Kahless in "Birthright" set up a subsequent story, also in the sixth season. In "Rightful Heir," written by Ronald D. Moore, and based on a story by James

E. Brooks, Worf has a crisis of faith.

Meeting the Klingon youths caused him to question his own commitment to the Klingon path. He asked himself if being in Starfleet turning his back on his people and culture.

A group of Klingon monks on the planet Boreth devote their entire lives to studying Kahless, teaching about the legendary Klingon warrior and predicting that he will one day return. Kahless is a Christ-like figure uniting Klingons in his teachings and the belief he will return to lead the people again. This belief has persisted for centuries.

Worf is one of a number of pilgrims on Boreth to undergo rituals, including one in a cavern sitting around a fire experiencing visions of Kahless. After several days, Worf becomes disenchanted because he experiences no visions.

Koroth, the leader of the acolytes of Kahless, points out that their faith demands patience. The Klingon people have been waiting for Kahless to return for 1500 years.

THE RETURN OF KAHLESS

A turning point in Klingon history occurs when Kahless returns during a fire ritual. At first they believe it another vision.

Worf realizes this isn't so. Kahless steps forward and greets them as Worf bears witness to a prophecy fulfilled.

This renews Worf's faith. It is proof Klingon beliefs are real. There is nothing like a doubter converted by a revelation.

Worf witnesses Kahless prove his identity to the acolytes. Kahless reveals the story of the forging of the bat'leth sword, a secret known only to the high clerics on Boreth. He is declared genuine, a legend returned to life to fulfill his 1500 year old pledge.

The return of Kahless is more than a religious event. It is a political event which directly effects the Klingon High Council.

Koroth wants Kahless taken to Klinzai, but fears Gowron will oppose his sudden appearance. Once again the politics of Klingon government come into play.

Gowron will resist stepping down after fighting to preserve his position in the recent civil war.

It is believed the Klingon people will elevate Kahless to be their leader by popular mandate. Although Worf witnessed the return of Kahless, when pressed for proof he admits he has no evidence.

THE CHALLENGE

The question of proving the identity of Kahless is again raised when Gowron intercepts the Enterprise. Gowron recognizes the symbolic importance of

Kahless. This figure from the past represents everything a Klingon fights for and strives to be.

The sacred knife of Kirom is presented to test the identity of Kahless. This knife bears a 1500 year old blood stain said to be that of Kahless. The living Kahless matches the blood. The last hurdle appears passed; Kahless has miraculously returned from the dead.

No scientific test can brand this Kahless a fake. Yet there is more to proving one's identity. To a Klingon action is everything.

Gowron challenges Kahless to fight. The outcome should not be in doubt. Kahless is the greatest Klingon warrior who ever lived.

When Gowron easily defeats him, even Worf realizes something is wrong. The legendary Kahless should not be easily defeated in hand-to-hand combat.

Under threat of death, Koroth and the acolytes reveal that Kahless is a clone created from the blood sample on the sacred knife of Kirom. He possesses all the knowledge they had about Kahless.

When first awakened as a full grown man he believed himself to be Kahless. The clone first appeared on Boroth by being beamed into the cavern in the first conscious moment of his life.

A POLITICAL COMPROMISE

Symbols are important. Even a clone of Kahless is closer to the real thing than the people of Klinzai have had for 1500 years.

Revealing the truth will not matter to many. Revolution will result if Gowron opposes giving Kahless a voice in the government.

A compromise is struck. Kahless will be named emperor, a title unused by Klingons for many years.

He will become the moral leader of Klinzai while Gowron remains the political leader as head of the High Council. Once again the Klingon political system has changed, this time under threat of a civil war.

Kahless will stabilize life on Klinzai as a symbol for all they believe. He personifies the heritage of the Klingon people.

Although he now knows what he is, Kahless accepts his position in Klingon society. He will carry on the teachings of the real Kahless as a vital part of modern Klingon society.

Until the introduction of Kahless it was unknown whether Klingons had a religion beyond their strict warrior code. Kahless is now far more than the villainous character in the original STAR TREK episode "The Savage Curtain."

Klingons have been conspicuously absent from DEEP SPACE NINE until recently. The Klingon ves-

sel Toh'kaht emerges from the wormhole weeks ahead of schedule in "Dramatis Personae." No sooner does it appear than it blows up.

The sole survivor, Hon-Tihl, beams into Ops on the space station. He lives only long enough to declare victory. Apparently the Klingons picked up an alien virus which caused them to replay the drama which brought about the end of an alien civilization.

The drama begins to be replayed on Deep Space Nine. The Klingons bear no further impact on the storyline.

BACK FROM THE PAST

Klingons appear in "Blood Oath," a second season DEEP SPACE NINE episode. Three very old Klingons, Kor, Koloth and Kang, arrive at the space station to settle an old debt.

Eighty years before, the three and Dax (Curzon Dax) had made a blood oath to kill the man responsible for the murder of their children. The long search is nearing its end.

While two Klingons don't mind that Dax is now a young woman, Kang is disturbed by this twist of fate. He refuses to hold her to Curzon's pledge. Dax is not as willing to forget and baits Kang into allowing her to accompany them.

Klingon honor is further defined in this episode. While Koloth and Kor are willing to accept Dax, Kang is not.

At first this appears to be simple male chauvinism, but this is a deliberate blind. Because Klingon warriors seem likely be chauvinistic, when Kang initially rejects Dax, the reason seems apparent, but Dax determines the truth.

Kang believes they are going into a trap. He expects to die in a last valiant attempt to avenge the death of his son. While he would have accepted the help of the man he remembers, and who would be nearing the end of his life, Kang was not willing to bring a young woman to her certain death.

Dax angers Kang, forcing him to relent. It is mentioned that Kang met Dax during the peace negotiations 80 years before the events in "Blood Oath." They became friends as a result of the armistice negotiations and Dax became godfather of Kang's son.

A few years later, when Kang's son and the sons of Kor and Koloth were killed by a vengeful man called "The Albino," Dax vowed to help track down and kill this murderer. The man remained elusive for many years, until Kang finally learned of the killer's whereabouts.

REUNION

The portrayal of Kang, Kor and Koloth is significant. Each character appeared as a villain in episodes of the original STAR TREK. They are played in DEEP SPACE NINE by the same actors, Kang by Michael Ansara ("Day Of The Dove"), Kor by John Colicos ("Errand Of Mercy") and Koloth by William Campbell ("The Trouble With Tribbles").

On Classic Trek none of these characters had a real personality. In "Blood Oath" they do.

Koloth takes over a holosuite and continually refights an old battle he is determined to win. He becomes drunk, and, when Odo shuts down the holosuite, is easily convinced he finally won.

Kor is furious over Koloth's reprehensible behavior and refuses to bail him out of his detention cell. Koloth is released after Kang arrives.

The three discuss their plans.

Dax, supposedly several hundred years old, has never killed. His friends have often been warriors and soldiers, but Dax goes to Major Kira to ask her what it's like to kill. This sounds more like Jadzia than Dax.

DYING FOR IDEALS

"Blood Oath" is unlike other DEEP SPACE NINE episodes. Its structure is more like many original STAR TREK episodes. It builds to a prolonged fight scene at the climax. Although the 24th century bristles with phaser beam weapons, Dax neutralizes them when they invade the compound. Combat is limited to knives and swords.

Klingons live and breathe for personal combat—not the ship to ship combat now common in which only the captain calls the shots. Klingons still train for hand to hand combat with a variety of bladed weapons they rarely get to use except on a holodeck.

In "Blood Oath" the Klingons come roaring in, slashing and cutting, taking out as many of the enemy

as they can, selling their lives dearly. Two of the Klingons die, but Kang gets his revenge. Before he perishes, he sees the murderer of his son killed before his eyes.

Kang, Kor and Koloth embody the deepest ideals of the Klingon empire. They fight for the honor of their family, ending their lives in glorious combat.

Kor cries the Klingon death chant for his two fallen comrades as the episode ends. The viewer is left wondering who is most fortunate, the survivor Kor or his two friends who died achieving their life-long quest for vengeance.

THE HOME WORLD

Klingons are a complicated people. THE NEXT GENERATION and DEEP SPACE NINE explain the background of these people making them one of the most interesting aspects of the 24th Century STAR TREK universe.

The Klingon home world is called Klinzai, although it is rarely used. Even its nickname, Kling, is rarely heard.

The High Council is the ruling body on the Klingon home world. Gowron is its leader. He wields the political power of the Klingon empire.

Once the enemies of the Federation, the Klingon Empire signed an armistice more than 80 years before. It was the aftermath of the destruction of the moon on which the Klingons manufactured the power used to supply Klinzai and the other worlds in the empire.

Despite the necessity of making peace for the survival of the empire, some Klingons tried to subvert the peace process to no avail. Today the Klingon Empire takes the peace treaty very seriously. It will not allow even one citizen of the empire to violate it. This was evident in "Heart Of Glory" in the first season of THE NEXT GENERATION.

HONORED RITUALS

Beginning with THE NEXT GENERATION, the Klingon culture has been explored. Most of the episodes focused on Worf and his interaction with other Klingons. Since Worf appears in nearly every episode of NEXT GENERATION, there have been constant asides, particularly since Worf's son Alexander became a recurring character.

Because Worf grew up with human foster parents, he missed the time honored rituals of Klingon youth. One is the Age of Ascension. In this ritual, a Klingon's closest friends form a gauntlet and beat him with pain sticks.

Worf recruits his friends aboard the Enterprise to carry this out in the holodeck. They are reluctant to comply, but Worf assures them it is a tremendous honor. Klingons do not shrink from pain but welcome it as a test of their mettle. The ritual is repeated on important anniversaries in a Klingon's life.

Patriarchy is important to the culture of the Klingons. The death of Worf's father when he was quite young remains a crucial event in his life. Veneration of the father involves the ritual of the Majqa.

The Majqa is a self-induced trance-like state that allows visions of a deceased father. In this way he hopes to learn important revelations of his patriarch that he might apply to his own life in a meaningful way.

A WARRIORS HONOR

Honor is vital to a Klingon from childhood. A Klingon child never lies; it not only dishonors him, but his parents as well.

Questioning a Klingon's honor can result in an immediate, deadly duel. Duels are common as Klingons do not fear death. To die in battle is the highest honor a Klingon can attain. To die of old age in bed is looked upon with disdain. A Klingon would sooner commit suicide than allow his life to end in a sickbed as an infirm old man.

A Klingon learns the names of his weapons and to venerate the empire's fighting heritage. A variety of weapons are used by a Klingon, even in a century when hand phasers are common and starships fight battles with incredible weapons of destruction.

The Gin'tak spear, although an ancient weapon, is still taught to the modern Klingon warrior. The weapon is used in duels and is ceremonial in nature. The Gin'tak is also used for target practice during the ritual of Qa'vak, a technique employed by Klingons to sharpen their skills with the Gin'tak.

Another bladed weapon is the Kut'luch. It is a knife used by assassins.

A less common warrior ritual is the "Klingon Tea Ceremony." Tea is not what participants drink. Instead they consume a beverage deadly to humans without a ready antidote. Thoroughly unpalatable to humans, this drink is relished by Klingons.

TECHNOLOGICAL SECRETS

Despite the alliance between Federation and Klingon Empire, a conflicting treaty with the Romulans prohibits the Federation from exploring "cloaking" technology.

Cloaking is a well established facet of Klingon starships. It makes a vessel invisible to both sensors and visual contact. There are intricate methods to scan for spacial disturbances relative to the movement of a cloaked ship.

A Klingon must always be in command of a cloaked vessel on a Starfleet mission. The discovery of cloaking technology is claimed by both Romulans and Klingons. It cannot be determined who discovered it a century ago when Romulans and Klingons were allies and adversaries of the Federation.

The technology has been so jealously guarded that not even the Ferengi have been able to buy the secret.

Romulans commonly employ this "stealth" technology, unlike Klingons who do not sneak up on a foe. Klingons prefer open combat where each adversary is fully aware of the other.

Eighty years before, when the Klingons looked to be facing extinction, their alliance with the Federation saved them. It enabled the Klingons to flourish as a race and retain their warrior heritage.

Only background characters in the original STAR TREK, Klingons emerged with a rich culture in the 24th Century. The philosophy and ideals of the Klingons contribute to the success of THE NEXT GENERATION and DEEP SPACE NINE. They could even star in a spin-off series.

Romulans have been a part of STAR TREK since the beginning. When they re-emerged in the 24th Century, this alien culture was explored in greater detail than before.

ROMULANS IN THE 24TH CENTURY

Aliens have always been a part of the STAR TREK universe. The Romulans were the first portrayed with a history intertwined with the Federation, in a previously fought war, and with Vulcan, in a never-before-suspected heritage.

The Romulan connection to Vulcan was first mentioned in the original STAR TREK, particularly in the episode "Balance Of Terror." The story introduced the Romulans to the STAR TREK universe.

Before joining 24th Century STAR TREK, Romulans were last seen in "The Enterprise Incident" in 1969. The STAR TREK motion pictures ignored them.

The first season finale of NEXT GENERATION returned the Romulans to the screen in the appropriately titled, "The Neutral Zone." Written by Maurice Hurley and based on a story by Deborah McIntyre and Mona Clee, the title refers to the Romulan Neutral Zone, established in Classic Trek's "Balance Of Terror."

In this NEXT GENERATION episode, the Romulans have remained silent behind their treaty imposed barrier for some 50 years. When outposts along the Neutral Zone mysteriously go silent, the Federation wonders whether they are becoming actively hostile.

The Enterprise is sent to investigate. The Romulans may be testing the Federation to see their technological advances of the past fifty years.

It is not revealed whether the Romulans already know. After all, being Vulcan offshoots, they could easily spy on the Federation passing themselves off as Vulcans. Since Vulcans are unemotional to the point of seeming standoffish, they could go about their mission without drawing any undue attention.

RENEWED CONTACT

The Enterprise finds two outposts destroyed. When a Romulan ship approaches, Picard maintains a neutral posture.

This is a historic moment—the first contact between the Romulans and the Federation in five decades. The Romulans reveal that their own outposts have also been attacked, but refuse to join forces with the Federation to investigate the mystery. They look upon the idea with disdain. They do not accuse Starfleet of attacking their outposts, although Worf is ready to believe the Romulans are behind the mystery.

In the early days of THE NEXT GENERATION, Worf hated Romulans. They had killed his father at Khitomer about twenty-five years before. Worf was about 7 when his real parents died.

The Romulans had already cut themselves off from the Federation, maintaining some contact with the Klingon Empire. It has never been revealed why the Romulans turned on the Klingons.

This initial contact between the Romulans and Starfleet ended with the Romulans saying they had been "busy with other things" for many years, but would not be silent any longer. They do not trust Starfleet any more than Starfleet trusts them.

24th Century Romulans go through various stages, from outright villains to inscrutable outsiders. While the Federation would like to establish diplomatic relations with the Romulans, they prefer to keep their distance.

AT THE EDGE OF THE NEUTRAL ZONE

This destruction of outposts on both sides of the Neutral Zone goes unresolved until the Borg are introduced two seasons later. Then, when the Borg threaten the Federation, the Romulans do not get involved. Their neutrality in the Borg war is not discussed. until "The Best Of Both Worlds."

Romulans have never appeared on DEEP SPACE NINE. It is odd they are not intrigued by the Bajoran Wormhole.

The Romulans make their next appearance when the Enterprise strays close to the Neutral Zone in the second season entry "Contagion," written by Steve Gerber and Beth Woods. When the Federation vessel Yamato is destroyed, clues lead to a planet close to the border of the Neutral Zone. This planet may be the legendary Iconia.

Iconia bears the remains of a civilization apparently destroyed in a war two hundred thousand years before. Rumors have persist that the Iconians possessed technology far surpassing that of the 24th Century.

THE SECRET OF THE GATEWAY

Iconia is not a dead world. The planet launches probes when a vessel approaches. These probes carry a computer virus capable of destroying the ship.

While exploring one of the ancient cities, the away team discovers an intact command center. Data learns how to make it work, tapping into a "gateway." The instant transportation is far more efficient and less risky than a transporter beam.

A Romulan ship suffering from the Iconian computer virus confronts the Enterprise and accuses them of sabotage. Captain Picard blows up the Iconian command center to keep the Romulans from discovering the "gateway."

To prove his good intentions, Picard helps the Romulans remove the virus. Whether this act of

kindness will impress the Romulans remains to be seen.

Starfleet mistrusts the Romulans. They do not want the Romulans to have the technology to create a gateway.

FRIENDS AND ENEMIES

Uniting with an enemy to survive mutual danger is an old idea. The plot emerges in "The Enemy," written by David Kemper and Michael Piller. The title of this episode will prove significant later in an episode titled "Face Of The Enemy."

Geordi is separated from his away team on a planet ravaged by electromagnetic storms. Meanwhile, the away team beams an injured Romulan to the Enterprise.

Geordi can't be located. He encounters another Romulan and is taken prisoner. Both are lost and must help each other to survive.

The injured Romulan on the Enterprise requires a blood transfusion to survive. Only Worf's blood will save him, but Worf refuses because the Romulans killed his parents.

The show does not cop out by synthesizing plasma or using another dodge. Worf refuses to help and the Romulan dies, with Worf expressing no regrets.

A Romulan rescue ship arrives just as the Enterprise rescues Geordi and the Romulan centurion. The Romulans claim only one man had been aboard the crashed vessel until the Enterprise produces the second crewman. The body of the dead Romulan and his rescued comrade are turned over to the Romulan vessel

This episode establishes the possibility that Romulans and humans can negotiate without being automatic enemies, despite the mutual hostility of Worf and the dying Romulan.

PLOT AND COUNTER- PLOT

Romulans consider themselves enemies of the Federation. This is illustrated in the third season episode "The Defector," written by Ronald D. Moore. The story offers the first glimpse inside Romulan culture.

When the Enterprise intercepts a small Romulan scout ship, they save its lone occupant from a warbird in hot pursuit. The pilot, an older Romulan, asks for asylum.

At first, he says he's a minor logistics officer who fled Romulan space with information of an impending attack on the Federation. He insists the Romulans are preparing for war and have established a base of operations inside the Neutral Zone.

Picard is skeptical, particularly since the claim can only be verified from within the Neutral Zone. If the Enterprise entered the Neutral Zone, the Romulans would have every right to retaliate.

When the defector is taken to the holodeck, Data recreates the lovely Valley of Chula, a place on Romulus where rare flowers only bloom in the evening. The defector knows he will never again visit this valley on his homeworld. The Romulan is an admiral sick of war. He believes the Romulan empire will destroy itself if it embarks on another destructive campaign against the Federation.

IN THE JAWS OF THE TRAP

When Data relates the incident, Captain Picard decides the Romulan's claim may be legitimate. The Enterprise penetrates the Neutral Zone, but finds the planetoid deserted. Two waiting Romulan warships decloak in a trap concocted to capture the Enterprise.

The Romulan admiral was not aware of the plot. He had been carefully manipulated to plant false information.

Picard reveals he suspected the trap. Then two Klingon warships decloak, ending the standoff. The Romulan ships return to Romulus.

After learning how he had been used, the admiral commits suicide, leaving behind a letter to his family. The letter cannot be delivered unless the Federation and the Romulans come to peace terms.

The Romulan admiral was willing to sacrifice his own life for the betterment of his people. This marked the first time a Romulan was shown to disagree with their policy of manifest destiny. There are parallels between this resistance to government polices and that of the Cardassians explored on DEEP SPACE NINE.

THE RACE TO BETA NIOBE

The Romulans are only mentioned in "Sins Of The Father." The episode refers to the Khitomer Massacre of which there were only two survivors, including a child named Worf. Recently retrieved Romulan records name a Klingon traitor whose information led to the massacre.

It is clear Klingons are as touchy about Romulans as Bajorans are about Cardassians. The Klingons and Romulans were once allies. Why they ended the alliance and the Romulans attacked Khitomer has not been revealed.

In the season three episode "Tin Man," written by Dennis Putman Bailey and David Bischoff, the Romulans make an appearance just as the Klingons periodically did in the original STAR TREK. The Romulans throw their weight around and make

demands in a matter of no concern to them.

When the Federation learns that a previously unknown life form (code name "Tin Man") has been detected by a probe circling a star that will soon go nova, the Enterprise is dispatched to make contact. Tin Man is a being, perhaps the last of its kind, who might only be described as a living spacecraft. It once shared a symbiotic alliance with a now dead race.

Tin Man is sentient. The Betazoid, Tam Elbrun, has been assigned to communicate with it and has already made contact over many light years.

Romulans intercepted the messages between Federation vessels and believe there is strategic significance in Tin Man. They don't want the Federation to gain an advantage by achieving first contact.

The Romulans attack and damage the Enterprise's shields, thus delaying the starship. This will enable the Romulans to contact Tin Man first.

TIN MAN DECIDES

Tam Elbrun had read the Romulans' minds when their ship attacked. He knows they mean to destroy Tin Man.

The Betazoid warns the entity of the intentions of the Romulans. Tin Man responds by destroying the Romulan attacker when it arrives at Beta Niobe where Tin Man waits for the star to go nova.

It hopes to end its own life. Its "crew" died long before and the ancient being waits to die—until Tam Elbrun beams aboard and becomes its new "crew."

When a second Romulan vessel attacks, Tin Man hurls both it and the Enterprise 3.8 billion kilometers away just as the star goes nova. No trace of Tam and Tin Man can be found. They were either destroyed or escaped into deep space,

never to be found again. The Romulans were defeated in their attempt to destroy this unique and powerful entity.

Apparently the Romulans knew Tin Man possessed great power. They feared it falling into the hands of the Federation.

The Romulans lacked a telepathic counterpart to Tam Elbrun. Although the Romulans are offshoots of the Vulcan race, the separation of cultures occurred before the Vulcans developed telepathic abilities; no Romulan has ever displayed talents such as Vulcans commonly possess.

BEHIND THE SCENES MANIPULATIONS

In "Reunion," written by Thomas Perry and Jo Perry and Ronald D. Moore and Brandon Braga from a story by Drew Deighan and Thomas Perry and Jo Perry, a Klingon traitor collaborates with the Romulans. A bomb explodes, killing two

aides, during the ritual of ascension to determine the new head of the Klingon High Council. It is a Romulan bomb. Again the Romulans are attempting to manipulate the inner workings of the Klingon government.

Romulans do not appear in "Reunion." The episode shows that the Romulans still want to control their old allies.

More Romulan treachery is revealed in another fourth season episode, "Data's Day." Vulcan Ambassador T'Pel secretly beams aboard the Enterprise to meet with Captain Picard. She is to be taken to the Romulan Neutral Zone for vital negotiations.

When a Romulan warbird arrives at the predetermined coordinates, T'Pel beams over to begin secret negotiations. This ends when a mysterious transporter malfunction apparently results in T'Pel's death, leaving only minute organic traces on the transporter pad.

The Enterprise departs, but investigations reveal that the traces are not of T'Pel. The Romulans altered their transporters to fake T'Pel's death.

Ambassador T'Pel wasn't a Vulcan, but a Romulan spy. How much she learned about the Federation remains unknown. How she fooled telepathic Vulcans is also unknown. Even half-Vulcan Ambassador Spock has full telepathic abilities.

PLOTTING A WAR

The Romulans are determined to make life difficult for the Klingons and the Federation. In the fifth season episode, "The Mind's Eye," written by Rene Echevarria from a story by Ken Schafer and Rene Echevarria, the Romulans kidnap Geordi. They brainwash him into becoming an assassin in a storyline not dissimilar from THE MANCHURIAN CANDIDATE.

Instead of manipulating an election, he is to drive a wedge between the Federation and the Klingons. The Romulans hope to shatter the 80 year old peace accord. They would then pick up the pieces after both Federation and Empire fall.

Geordi is programmed to kill Governor Vagh of K'Reos, a Klingon colony experiencing a war for independence. The Enterprise is framed as supplying weapons to the rebels.

Data shows that the weapons the Klingons intercepted are clever forgeries manufactured by Romulan technology. The Klingons are suspicious.

Governor Vagh can't guess that Kell, the Klingon ambassador to K'Reos, is the real traitor collaborating with the Romulans. Kell wants Governor Vagh to beam up and supervise the investigation on board the Enterprise. LaForge then will kill Vagh in front of witnesses and claim that he was acting on orders from the Federation.

Data warns security in time for Worf to avert the assassination. When Ambassador Kell is confronted with the evidence of his involvement in the assassination plot, he demands asylum on the Enterprise. Picard says that after he is searched by the Klingons he will be granted refuge on the Enterprise.

Kell is arrested and beamed down to K'Reos. The viewer can only imagine the methods the Klingons will employ to "search" Kell for the evidence of his collaboration with Romulans.

It is not clear what enticement the Romulans offered the Klingon to persuade him to betray his own people. Not only do Klingons hate Romulans, but Klingon treatment of traitors is notorious.

A TRAITOROUS LEGACY

"Redemption," written by Ronald D. Moore, again features Romulan subterfuge. Traitors within the Klingon Empire collaborate to give Romulans the power behind the throne.

The Duras sisters' father betrayed Klinzai at Khitomer years before. Now they collaborate with the Romulans, even after seeing the downfall and disgrace brought upon their father and brother.

The sisters concoct a scheme to pass a Klingon youth off as their brother's illegitimate son, and rightful heir to the family seat on the High Council. The Romulans secretly support this bid, supplying the sisters with armaments and supplies in the civil war against Gowron, leader of the High Council.

The Klingon civil war forces warriors to choose sides. When Klingons fight, particularly each other, no quarter is given or asked. The war could easily destroy Klingon society. This is why when the clone of Kahless emerged, Gowron chose a workable compromise rather than face another civil war.

THE TASHA YAR CONNECTION

During the Klingon civil war, the Enterprise contacts a Romulan vessel commanded by a woman named Sela. She looks exactly like Tasha Yar, the deceased Enterprise security officer.

When Sela and Captain Picard meet, she tells him Tasha Yar was her mother. Although Picard finds this difficult to believe, she insists Tasha was on the Enterprise-C at the battle of Khitomer. She says that when the vessel successfully defended the Klingon colony, Tasha was among those taken prisoner.

Tasha became the consort of a Romulan general in exchange for sparing the other prisoners. Five years later, when Tasha attempted to escape from Romulus with her four year old daughter, the child gave the alarm. Tasha was captured and executed.

Sela describes these events in very dispassionate terms. She insists her humanity died with her mother. Sela is full Romulan now and proud of it.

Sela is confident the Duras sisters will triumph. When the Federation cuts the Romulan supply line, the civil war goes in favor of Gowron. Sela becomes a bitter enemy of Picard. The time will come when she finds herself able to get the best of not only Picard, but a founding member of the Federation as well.

THE VULCAN AFFAIR

"Unification" is a two-part episode of THE NEXT GENERATION. The first part is written by Jeri Taylor from a story by Rick Berman and Michael Piller; part two is written by Michael Piller from a story by Rick Berman and Michael Piller.

The story offers the first close look of Romulus, the Romulan homeworld. The planet never before appeared in any version of STAR TREK.

"Unification," the story title, refers to the shared history of Vulcans and Romulans. Romulans split off from the Vulcan culture thousands of years before. Ambassador Spock learns there is a movement on Romulus to reunite the two divergent cultures.

Unfortunately, Vulcans and Romulans have little in common. Romulans are as similar to Vulcans as to humans; there is only overall physical resemblance. They are as far apart in philosophy as their planets are in geography.

Romulans have more in common with Klingons, whom they hate, than Vulcans. Their society resembles that of the Cardassians, a government run by a military not tolerant of dissent.

Vulcans are peaceful, a founding member of the Federation. They willingly abandoned a violent heritage to adopt a philosophy of peace during the Vulcan Reformation.

Vulcans are not born without emotions. They adopt the philosophy in childhood. Vulcans train not to express emotions when quite young. By the time they reach adulthood, it is as natural to them as breathing.

DIVERGENT PATHS

Romulans have no such philosophy. They continue the violent heritage of pre-Reformation Vulcan. They believe in a manifest destiny in which all races become subservient to Romulans. Their alliance with the Klingons collapsed twenty-five years before when they attacked the Klingon colony at Khitomer.

In "Unification" Spock journeys to Romulus. He meets with the Reunification underground to determine their size. Because Spock informs no one in the Federation of his trip, there is suspicion he has defected.

The first view of Romulan society occurs when Data and Picard, disguised as Romulans, beam down from a cloaked Klingon vessel. They contact the Reunification underground. Before they are spirited away, they enter a sidewalk cafe in a heavily populated area. It seems to be a poorer section of town.

Romulan security officers are everywhere. The government doesn't trust its subjects. Leaders only feel secure with a huge police force.

Data and Picard are taken to a cavern to meet with Spock. They also meet members of the Reunification underground who study books about life on Vulcan.

These people, many of them young, long for a society that is not infested with secret police and does not have an economy based on war. They embrace the lifestyle of peace and prosperity enjoyed by their Vulcan brothers and sisters. They explore new ways of living that can benefit all Romulans.

ENGULF AND DEVOUR

The Romulan government is aware of the Reunification movement. It found a way to use it to their own ends.

The government intends to send a captured Vulcan shuttle back to Vulcan while Spock (or a simulation) broadcasts a message announcing that the shuttle contains a Romulan peace envoy. Three cloaked Romulan ships filled with shock troops will follow the shuttle and penetrate the Vulcan security net. The ships will invade and conquer that planet before the Federation can respond.

The plan would cause a war between the Federation and Romulus. The Federation now includes a hundred planets while the Romulan Empire, behind the barriers of the Neutral Zone, is nowhere near as large.

The plot fails when the Enterprise guesses trickery is involved. The exposed Romulans destroy their transport ships, and the two thousand troops aboard them, to prevent their capture. This cannot help recruitment.

A warrior race strives to die in combat, not at the hands of their own commanders. If the Reunification movement isn't a threat to the government, the military's casual extermination of its own best and brightest must be.

On Romulus, Ambassador Spock tells Picard and Data that he intends to remain behind. He wants to work with the Reunification movement to bring about real change so unification of their peoples, without violence or coercion, can come to pass.

Spock does not appear in the NEXT GENERATION motion picture. What remains is speculative.

TECHNOLOGICAL THREAT

Spock's progress is unknown, but it doesn't take long to discover what the Romulans are up to. Later in the fifth season, in the episode "The Next Phase," written by Ronald D. Moore, the Enterprise encounters a damaged Romulan ship. They agree to render aid.

A new phase of Federation/Romulan relations has begun. Starfleet has always been leery of direct contact with Romulans. Captain Picard has no problem agreeing to render humanitarian assistance so the Romulans can repair their vessel and return home.

The Romulans are really engaged in an experiment involving interphase technology. This cloaking device would make someone not only invisible, but intangible as well. They could pass through solid objects.

After what seems to be a transporter malfunction, everyone thinks Geordi and Ensign Ro are dead. They have been transformed by the interphase generator. They are invisible and intangible except to a Romulan who has also been transformed.

THE PRICE OF SUSPICION

The Romulans fear the Enterprise personnel will discover their closely guarded military secret. To insure it is not revealed, the Romulans plan to destroy the Enterprise. If there is any question whether the Romulan military has softened, this quickly removes those doubts.

The story focuses on the transformed Romulan. He tries to kill Georgi and Ro Laren.
The secret device creates unanswered questions. If subjects can move through walls, and the Romulan is ultimately defeated by hurling him through the exterior hull, how can they run along the corridors without slipping through the floor and into space? How can they see or speak? Light would not reflect off their retinas to create images and air would not be vibrated by their vocal cords to form sound.

They cannot eat. How does an intangible body function? None of these questions are asked or answered in the episode.

Romulans return in spirit in the sixth season episode "Rascals." When Ferengi hijack the Enterprise, they admit their customer is the Romulans.

RETURN OF THE UNDERGROUND

The Reunification movement reappears in the sixth season episode "Face Of The Enemy." Written by Naren Shankar from a story by Rene Eschevarria, this time the Romulans make the first move.

To smuggle out important members of the unification movement, Romulan sympathizers kidnap Deanna Troi. They surgically alter her to appear Romulan.

They don't ask her; they just do it. Apparently Deanna is an expert on Romulans. Kidnapping is a reckless act that could easily have doomed the entire mission.

"Face Of The Enemy" presents the first good look inside a Romulan ship since the original STAR TREK episode "Balance Of Terror." The Classic Trek episode "The Enterprise Incident" took place on board a Klingon ship the Romulans were using, so that didn't count.

SACRIFICES

Deanna Troi is masquerading as Major Rakal

of the Tal Shiar aboard the Romulan warship the Khazara. The Tal Shiar is a new addition to the lexicon of Romulan culture. They are the secret police.

Aboard a warship, the Tal Shiar even have authority over the commander. Commanders don't welcome the Tal Shiar. Troi stands up to the penetrating anger of the commander of the warbird.

The episode introduces an ex-Federation ensign who defected to the Romulans years before and has seen the error of his ways. He returns after seeing life on Romulus and wants to help the Federation deal with the unification movement. To prove his legitimacy, he brings a message from Spock that leads the Federation to a rendezvous point.

Key members of the Romulan underground placed in stasis are now transferred. These include Vice Proconsul M'ret of the Imperial Romulan Senate

and his two top aides. The mission opens an escape route for Romulan dissidents who wish to defect.

N'Vek, the Romulan who "recruited" Troi, is killed while protecting her. She escapes to the Enterprise. On the Enterprise, Picard declares the mission a success. Future dissidents will be able to escape.

N'Vek's sacrifice was not in vain. "Face of the Enemy" shows the faces of Romulans who oppose the iron rule of their military government.

TRAPPED BY HONOR

One Romulan military leader breaks the mold. Tokath takes pity on his prisoners when they cannot return to their home world. The Romulan command gives him the choice of executing the Klingon prisoners or overseeing them from then on.

Tokath has married a Klingon woman and refuses to allow Worf to disrupt

their lives. This is the only Romulan/Klingon inter-marriage shown. When Worf encounters Ba'el, Tokath's daughter, the Klingon is repulsed at the thought of a Klingon/Romulan hybrid.

Tokath is a gentle Romulan man. He and his fellow Romulans, and the Klingon families, have lived in peace for more than twenty years since the Khitomer Campaign. When Worf threatens to disrupt their tranquillity, Tokath orders him to live in peace or face execution.

Worf tells tales of Klingon heritage, firing the enthusiasms of Klingon youth in the encampment. They stand with Worf, insisting that if Worf dies then they must die too, as a Klingon should.

Faced with a mini-insurrection, Tokath relents. Worf promises to keep the world a secret. Tokath agrees to allow Worf and the Klingon youths to leave, another sign he is not an average Romulan.

A SENTIMENTAL ROMULAN

Tokath is the first ranking Romulan military officer who displays peaceful intent and shows a compassionate side. He could be compared to the Romulan commander in "Balance Of Terror," the original STAR TREK episode that introduced the Romulans in 1966.

Tokath seems war weary, not really part of the Romulan military industrial complex. Someone volunteering to spend his career as a camp commandant is not looking for advancement up the military ladder.

Tokath is the prison guard for people who have no wish to escape. To these Klingons, returning to their homeworld would be the worst thing that could happen to them.

Their children know nothing about the truth of why they're there. They believe they live there because a war is raging on Klinzai.

When Worf leaves with the Klingon youths, Ba'el remains behind with her family. She finally understands she could never be accepted in Klingon or Romulan society. Only on that small world can she find acceptance.

Most Klingons and Romulans would find Ba'el abhorrent. A product of love and understanding between members of opposing cultures, Ba'el would find herself a pariah on Klinzai or Romulus.

BROTHERS?

The Romulans appear at the climax of "The Chase," written by Joe Menosky. After the Enterprise searches the galaxy for DNA code samples, they arrive at a world in the Vilmoran system. As soon as an away team beams down, it is confronted by Romulans who have been secretly observing the Enterprise.

When the completed code reveals a hologram proving all humanoid life forms in the Alpha Quadrant have a common background, the Romulans respond in a positive way. The Romulan commander suggests that perhaps one day their people will come together in fellowship, just as their creators intended they should.

This could mark a turning point in the history of relations between the Federation and the Romulans.

A MATTER OF TIME

The Romulans are supporting characters later in season six in the episode "Timescape," written by Brannon Braga. At first they appear to be the villains again, but that ready assumption is a trick.

The Enterprise aids a stricken Romulan vessel, but both are caught in a time-space pocket. When the shuttle containing Picard, Data, Geordi and Troi returns to rendezvous with the Enterprise, they see the two ships frozen in time. It seems the Romulan ship is attacking the Enterprise. This proves untrue as the Romulans were not at fault.

This is the first time Romulans pose no threat to Federation personnel. It may preview the new direction for relations the conclusion of "The Chase" hinted at. Romulans may be on a gradual road towards the kind of armistice the Klingons signed some 80 years before.

CONTROVERSY

In season seven the Romulans return in the episode "Pegasus." It has become controversial because it involves the search by the Enterprise for the USS Pegasus, the first vessel on which William

Riker served after graduating from Starfleet Academy. Although thought destroyed years before, evidence points to the ship having survived and become lodged inside an asteroid belt near the Romulan Neutral Zone.

When the Enterprise begins searching for the vessel, the Romulans become suspicious. Picard finds the Pegasus inside a huge cavern inside a planetoid. The Enterprise enters to search for it, only to be sealed up by the suspicious Romulans.

The Pegasus had been testing a secret phasing cloak to turn ships invisible and intangible. It is used to help the Enterprise escape.

Picard immediately contacts the Romulans and informs them Starfleet has violated a treaty. He states that any Starfleet personnel involved in this experiment will face a court martial.

Does a starship captain have the right to take such an action after the experi-

ment has been approved by the highest levels of Starfleet? Viewers could not accept anyone in the 20th Century military blowing the whistle on the brass. However, Gene Roddenberry often said Starfleet is not a military organization.

A MEETING
OF THE MINDS?

Over the past seven years THE NEXT GENERATION has revealed much about the Romulans while DEEP SPACE NINE illuminated nothing. The Romulans remain uninterested in the wormhole.

There are two Romulan home worlds in a double-star system. The worlds are called Romulus and Remus, although these are galactic standard translations of the actual Romulan names for them.

Although little of the world was shown in the two part episode "Unification," in an earlier episode, "The Defector," various areas were discussed, including the Apnex Sea and the firefalls of Gal'gathong. There is also mention of the Chula Valley and its unique wild flowers which only bloom at night. It is a picturesque vision of a beautiful world very unlike its history of violence and militarism.

Romulans opt for suicide when faced with capture. This trait goes back to their first appearance in "Balance Of Terror" when Captain Kirk offers to lend aid to the crippled Romulan vessel. The commander replies, "That is not our way" just before he destroys his ship.

Romulan women serve with equality in their military, commanding starships and setting policy. Officers in the Romulan secret police, the Tal Shi'ar, are often female. Their orders are never questioned. Despite harsh, police-state life on the Romulan homeworlds, the Romulan military may be opening diplomatic channels with the Federation.

However one views Picard's actions revealing Federation treaty violations to the Romulans, this can only impress them with the honesty of Starfleet. On the other hand, Romulans may interpret this differently. They may decide Starfleet is more like them than they had believed.

Turning in fellow officers for dereliction of duty would be encouraged in a police state. However, no Romulan would ever reveal the private mechanizations of his government to an opposing power lest his career and his life be suddenly shortened.

This begs the question—are Romulans becoming more like the Federation or is the Federation becoming more like the Romulans? Seven years of contact on THE NEXT GENERATION have shown changes revealing possibilities.

The end chapter on Romulan/Federation relations has yet to be written, but chances of it repeating that of Klingon/Federation relations are much stronger now than seven years ago. Seven years ago the possibility seemed unlikely. Now that possibility exists.

How do you battle an invincible nemesis, who, though human, cannot conceive of compassion? These beings from beyond have altered the tapestry of life in the STAR TREK universe of the 24th Century.

THE BORG: THE ULTIMATE INVADERS

When STAR TREK—THE NEXT GENERATION began, they no longer had the Klingons to kick around any more. No longer stock villains, the Klingons were allies of the Federation.

The change came some time between the end of the original STAR TREK series and the beginning of the NEXT GENERATION. How this happened was finally revealed in the motion picture STAR TREK VI: THE UNDISCOVERED COUNTRY.

At first THE NEXT GENERATION tried to fill the void with a new alien race, the Ferengi. Creative shortcomings, most notably their height, made them less than the imposing adversaries they were at first intended to be. Instead they degenerated into comedy relief.

Romulans tried to regain their old stature as powerful antagonists, but viewers knew the

Federation had already beaten them in one war and fenced them behind a Neutral Zone. Despite their continuing threat, the Romulans weren't high-handed, fearless Empire builders such as the Klingons.

THE NEXT GENERATION needed a supremely powerful villain who could challenge Federation, Romulans, Klingons and anyone else in their way.

Enter the Borg.

FIRST CONTACT

The groundwork for the Borg began in the final episode of the first season of THE NEXT GENERATION. An unsolved subplot in "The Neutral Zone" concerned the mysterious destruction of outposts on both sides of the Neutral Zone.

The Borg finally appear in the third season episode "Q Who?." Q wants Picard to make him a crew member, so he takes the Enterprise to a distant

galaxy seven thousand light years from the Alpha Quadrant, in system J-25. The starship encounters the Borg.

They attack the ship and kill some crew members. It isn't evident if the Borg were interested in the Federation before this. They track the Enterprise down after this confrontation.

Would they have done this if Q hadn't caused the confrontation? Only the mysteriously destroyed outposts in "The Neutral Zone" indicate that the Borg had visited once before. In a later episode, "The Best Of Both Worlds," the destroyed outposts are linked to the Borg.

Q says the Federation must be prepared to meet the Borg, because they will come. It can be argued that Q helped prepare the Federation for battle with the supremely powerful cyborgs they may otherwise have been unaware of until the race suddenly invaded.

THE BORG COLLECTIVE

The cybernetic Borg are born fully human. Immediately after birth, mechanical devices are attached to begin the transformation into a part of the Borg collective, a massive hive mind.

All individuality and personality are submerged for the good of the many. Borg society has no concept of individuality. A Borg separated from the collective is helpless as all Borg are linked and think in tandem.

The Borg never negotiate. They exist only to absorb societies they encounter and destroy those who resist.

The second encounter with the Borg occurred in the two-part episode titled "The Best Of Both Worlds." The Federation has been preparing for a Borg attack for two years.

When the New Providence Colony on Jeray IV is obliterated,

magnetic resonance traces confirm that the Borg destroyed the colony and killed 900 colonists. A distress call from a Federation ship leads the Enterprise to the waiting Borg.

The Borg have been waiting for Jean-Luc Picard. They remember him from a previous encounter.

They hail Picard by name and beam him over to their vessel. Then they ignore the Enterprise and continue their previous heading, which will eventually take them to Earth.

LOCUTUS OF BORG

Invaders on STAR TREK always pick on Earth. True to form, the Borg aim the brunt of their invasion at Earth. It is the headquarters of Starfleet Command, but the Federation is spread over 100 worlds. Earth is an important world in the Federation, but so are Vulcan and Klinzai.

Picard is transformed into a Borg in record time as ordinary Borg are grown from birth. He is given the full treatment, remade into Locutus of Borg.

Locutus becomes their spokesman dealing with the Federation. Why a race that subverts individuality has names is not clear. A later episode indicates they have numbers that indicate their position inside the ship they live on.

Picard, or rather, Locutus, is so much a part of the Borg team they have complete access to his memories. This includes the defensive measures the Enterprise will adopt in combating them.

The Borg arrived nearly a year before the Federation expected them. They do not have new weapons ready so an armada of forty starships is assembled at Wolf 359.

At one point the script was going to include the Romulans, the story uniting Federation and Romulans against a common foe. Reportedly Gene Roddenberry didn't like the idea. Not including or mentioning the Romulans leaves the impression they just sat back to see whether the Federation might be suitably weakened for later advantage.

AFTERMATH

The Borg leave the Enterprise behind when they engage the Federation battlefleet. By the time the Enterprise arrives at Wolf 359, the fleet has been decimated.

Using a saucer separation as a diversion, Worf and Data recapture Picard. Aboard the Enterprise, they try to reconvert him to his complete humanity.

Picard gives Data a clue how to defeat the Borg. Their regenerative system can be manipulated to make them think it is time to sleep. This leads to a power feedback and the Borg ship self-destructs.

It takes time for Picard to recover from the experience. He experiences fallout up to and including the DEEP SPACE NINE episode, "The Emissary." The episode marks the only appearance of the Borg on DEEP SPACE NINE, although it is a crucial contact.

Picard confronts his residual demons in "Family," the episode that immediately followed "The Best Of Both Worlds." He tells his brother what he went through and reveals his personal agony for the first time.

Says Picard of the Borg: "They took everything I was. They used me to kill and to destroy and I couldn't stop them. I should have been able to stop them! I tried so hard, but I wasn't strong enough. I wasn't good enough. I should've been able to stop them!"

The Borg return on an exploratory mission on the edge of the Alpha Quadrant, an uncharted region of the galaxy. A distress call alerts the Enterprise to the presence of a crashed Borg scout ship.

They rescue the sole survivor, beaming him aboard the Enterprise even though the distress call will attract the Borg mother ship. The young Borg male is put in a holding cell.

Geordi blocks the homing signal to prevent him being followed to the Enterprise. Having a Borg on the Enterprise brings back bitter memories to Jean-Luc Picard.

THE THREAT OF INDIVIDUALITY

Picard opposes helping the Borg, yet Geordi finds he can communicate with the alien once the young man grows accustomed to the holding cell.

At first a plan is conceived to use the Borg to destroy the collective. An alternative plan is finally adopted. Geordi, and then some of the other crew members, have come to realize this Borg has a personality, and eventually even give him a name, Hugh.

Hugh is allowed to return, a Borg who has learned of individuality and that it is not to be feared. The Borg now have a human face and are no longer only villain and destroyer. Personalizing the Borg created new possibilities for future stories.

The Borg weren't seen again until the finale of the sixth season. In the episode "Descent," the Enterprise encounters a mysterious vessel orbiting the planet Ohniaka III, a ship that turns out to be a new kind of Borg vessel. When an away team beams down to the outpost, they discover that the entire staff has been murdered. The killers, a team of Borg, are still at the scene of the crime.

A BORG ALLIANCE

The Borg ship employs a "transwarp conduit" to jump through space without using warp drive. For the first time, Borg and humans wage personal combat, and Data kills one with his bare hands.

A subplot involves Data's evil brother, Lore. Lore has made himself the leader of renegade Borg while a splinter group under the leadership of Hugh opposes Lore's plans.

When Picard released Hugh in the fifth season, no one questioned the decision. In "Descent" he is confronted by Starfleet for his actions.

In the end Hugh and his group of Borg are portrayed as individuals who pose no threat to the Federation, but rather to the Borg collective. Picard's decision in releasing Hugh to his people may prove to be a good choice after all.

THE VICTIMS OF LOCUTUS

The location of the Borg homeworld is unknown. Except for the ship used by the Borg rebels in "Descent," the Borg vessel is the cube-shaped ship sees in "Q-Less" and "The Best Of Both Worlds."

The Borg have not played a major role on DEEP SPACE NINE, but they have had some impact.

The premiere episode, titled "The Emissary," introduced Commander Benjamin Sisko and his son, Jake. They were on a vessel at the battle of Wolf 359. Ben's wife, Jake's mother, died in the Borg attack and Ben was left emotionally scarred by the ordeal.

Ben Sisko hates the Borg, but he has not had to deal with them. He has confronted his hatred for Jean-Luc Picard, who, as Locutus, commanded the Borg ship that decimated the Federation fleet.

When Picard visits the space station shortly after Ben arrives, Sisko borders on hostility. Only after the Prophets, the beings who created the wormhole, confront Sisko with the memory of his wife dying in his arms, is he able to let go of his hatred. Only then can he get on with his life, forgiving Jean-Luc and accepting that Picard is also a victim.

MARK OF THE BORG

The first episode of DEEP SPACE NINE established the shared universe with THE NEXT GENERATION in a very dramatic way. It included flashbacks from the premiere episode of the fifth season of NEXT GENERATION. DEEP SPACE NINE offered the point of view of those who fought the Borg and lost, unlike that of the Enterprise that fought the Borg and won.

Since their introduction in the third season of THE NEXT GENERATION, the Borg have been significant to 24th Century Star Trek. They have posed a threat in both THE NEXT GENERATION and DEEP SPACE NINE.

DEEP SPACE NINE introduced not only the Bajoran wormhole but an entire new quadrant of the galaxy. The previously unknown worlds are now accessible to the Federation.

MYSTERIES INSIDE
THE GAMMA QUADRANT

DEEP SPACE NINE introduced the first stable wormhole in STAR TREK lore. The concept first appeared in the NEXT GENERATION episode "The Price." The episode introduced the unstable Barzan wormhole. The end of the wormhole in the Alpha Quadrant is stable, but the other end, in the Gamma Quadrant, changes position by hundreds of light years.

When the wormhole near Bajor was discovered in the premiere episode of DEEP SPACE NINE, it became a pivotal element of STAR TREK in the 24th Century. It opened a realm 70 thousand light years away—the Gamma Quadrant.

The Gamma Quadrant is filled with planets and people never seen before. The Gamma Quadrant opening of the wormhole always opens at the same point, five light years from the Idran System. Idran is a double-star system with type "O" stars, but no class M (Earth-like) worlds. Inhabited planets lie further afield.

The wormhole is home to the beings sometimes referred to as "The Prophets." This strange non-human race constructed the wormhole. Ben Sisko taught them the concept of linear time. For them all time exists simultaneously. Sequestered in their wormhole, The Prophets had never encountered other races.

THE WORLDS INSIDE

The first race encountered at Deep Space Nine was the Wadi. They revealed little other than that they are addicted to playing games, particularly the 24th Century equivalent of video games. When they were finished playing their games, they left, quite satisfied. They didn't stick around for diplomatic meetings.

The Wadi are essentially harmless, if preoccupied. The same cannot be said of the Rakhar. While they have never come through the wormhole to Deep Space Nine, the oppressive government of that world made clear that they execute dissidents. The accused are never put on trial.

The strangest world yet seen in the Gamma Quadrant is a moon .35 light years from the wormhole in what was believed to be an uninhabited double-star system. The moon is a prison planet surrounded by monitoring satellites. The monitors generate an artificial microbe used to bring dead prisoners back to life so they can complete their sentence, no matter how many times they die in battle.

A body returned to life this way becomes reliant on the microbes to survive. It can never leave the world, lest it die the final death from which there is no reawakening.

REALMS UNKNOWN

An early contact with the Gamma Quadrant proved disastrous for a Klingon survey vessel. The Klingons discovered strange energy spheres containing residual impressions of an ancient race. The Saltah'na had destroyed itself long before.

The spheres, called Thalmerite devices, recorded the plots and counterplots that destroyed the Saltah'na. They passed the recorded paranoia on to the Klingons on board the survey ship. It caused their destruction in the same way it earlier destroyed the Saltah'na. History tragically repeated itself.

A being known as a Tosk emerged from the Gamma Quadrant and visited Deep Space Nine. Tosks are intelligent beings raised to be the object of an interplanetary hunt. A Tosk's only purpose is to elude, fight and die when cornered.

Tosks are trained to feel humiliation if they survive a hunt. This is not a concept easily understood by residents of the Alpha Quadrant.

Archeological relics have been discovered in the Varath system of the Gamma Quadrant. A statue of Drolock, the Prime Asemtry of the Verath System during the 19th Dynasty, was found.

Thirty thousand years before, the civilization of the Verath System linked two dozen star systems. It is but history now.

Some planets in the Gamma Quadrant are rich in deuridium; Stakoron II possesses large deposits of Miszindol ore.

Not all regions of the Gamma Quadrant contain planets. As in the Alpha Quadrant, some regions are treacherous. On such area, the Chamra Vortex, contains pockets of the volatile substance Toh Maire. It can be detonated by the disturbances made by passing space craft.

WHO IS THE DOMINION?

The Prophets created the wormhole. They are a race never before encountered by the Federation. While contact has been made, humanoids and Prophets remain inscrutable to each other. The Prophets are peaceful and pose no threat as far as is known.

"The Dominion" are another matter. In "Rules Of Acquisition," it was revealed that The Dominion control all major commerce in the Gamma Quadrant. No one in the Federation has yet encountered one of The Dominion.

A slave race, the Scrians escaped from their home planet in the Gamma Quadrant when their masters were conquered by the Dominion. The escaped refugees number three million people.

The Dominion had no interest in keeping these people enslaved. How the Dominion wield such great power and what their goals are remain mysteries.

The Gamma Quadrant is a new addition to STAR TREK in the 24th Century. It has been the principal province of DEEP SPACE NINE while the Enterprise conducts its searches and encounters elsewhere. Whether the Enterprise will ever pass through the wormhole into the Gamma Quadrant remains to be seen.

Although Sarek appeared in THE NEXT GENERATION before his son did, it was the crossover of Spock that had the biggest impact of any event in the first five years of the new series.

SPOCK IN THE 24TH CENTURY

Spock may be the primary figure of the STAR TREK mythos. Spock inevitably edged out Kirk as the icon who most symbolized STAR TREK. When the first motion picture was made, the cast was not considered complete until Leonard Nimoy signed to return as Spock. Only then did they feel they had the elements in place for the definitive STAR TREK revival.

When Spock died in the second motion picture, it was the pivotal event. Spock's resurrection in STAR TREK III—THE SEARCH FOR SPOCK was the focal point of that film. The later films continued to depend on Spock for their most memorable scenes.

When STAR TREK—THE NEXT GENERATION began, Leonard Nimoy discounted the possibility of the new STAR TREK's success. "You can't catch lightning in a bottle twice," he was quoted as saying in 1987. He would later admit he was mistaken.

In 1991 Nimoy did more than revise his opinion of the NEXT GENERATION. He agreed to guest star on the show.

"Unification," the two-part episode which first aired in November 1991, completed a process begun earlier. When the third season episode "Sarek" brought Spock's father into the 24th Century, viewers guessed Spock wouldn't follow far behind.

"Sarek" established that the Vulcan ambassador suffered from a rare disorder only afflicting older Vulcans, a Vulcan version of Alzheimer's disease. Picard helps Sarek accept the debilitating ailment. Underlying the episode, albeit unspoken, was the thought Spock must also be alive!

It set the stage for Classic Trek's key figure to enter THE NEXT GENERATION. While "Sarek" established a tangible link between the two series, bringing back one of the main characters from the 23rd Century STAR TREK would cement the connection.

Nimoy was approached to appear on NEXT GENERATION. He requested a fee beyond the scope of the series budget. As time went on and this new STAR TREK became increasingly successful, Paramount came to terms with Nimoy. Two years after "Sarek" opened a galaxy of possibilities, Spock made his grand entrance.

THE DEFECTOR

Everyone knew Spock would appear in "Unification." In the first half of the two-part episode, Spock appeared as a fuzzy image on an intelligence photograph taken on Romulus, a home world of the Romulans. The Federation feared he was defecting.

The scene established that Spock was no longer with Starfleet but had followed in his father's footsteps and become an ambassador. Earlier in Spock's life, he had fought with Sarek because Spock had chosen to join Starfleet. Now, a century later, his Starfleet career is behind him and he's joined the Vulcan ambassador corps.

"Unification" doesn't explain why Spock and Sarek have suffered another falling out during the past seventy-five years. This estrangement persisted until Sarek's death while Spock is on Romulus.

Had Spock known his father was dying, he would have raced to his side. Sarek revealed to Picard that if Spock was on Romulus, he went without informing his family of his plans.

ROMULAN DISSENT

Spock went to Romulus to contact the unification underground, a group devoted reuniting the Romulan and Vulcan peoples as they were two thousand years before. Vulcan is the mother race of the Romulans.

In the strict, militaristic society of the Romulans, such beliefs are forbidden. Books discussing such things are banned. Because Spock has been a proponent of unification in the Federation, he has been contacted by sympathizers who asked him to come to Romulus and meet with them.

This looks suspicious to the Federation. Spock neither asked for, nor received, permission to enter the Neutral Zone and travel to the Romulan home world. Without official permission, Spock appears to be hiding something. The Federation fears he's defecting.

Sarek revealed to Picard that Spock is acquainted with Pardek, a Romulan senator. Spock met Pardek during ambassadorial duties. The Vulcan is believed to maintain open contact with the Romulans.

The first appearance of Spock occurs on Romulus in the last scene of the first part of "Unification." Pardek takes Picard and Data (disguised as Romulans) to a secret cavern. Spock emerges from the darkness to speak with them.

THE LOST TRIBE OF VULCAN

Spock is annoyed. He knew the Federation would oppose his mission. If the Federation learned his plans, they may be discovered by the Romulans.

Spock insists his peace mission is a personal one of no concern to Starfleet. That he is an official Starfleet representative does not concern him.

Spock is drawn to Romulan youth who dream of a better future. They want to learn Vulcan philosophy, a way of thinking very different from the Romulan way of life.

Spock is looked up to as a teacher and a master who can lead them to this new planetary order. This new order involves the reunification of the Vulcan and Romulan peoples.

At the time the tribe later known as the Romulans split off from the Vulcans, all Vulcans were very similar in temperament. Vulcans then were similar to Romulans now. They were warlike and driven by intense emotion.

The tribe that became the Romulans decided that rather than continue fighting other tribes, they could establish their own way of life on another world. It wasn't until the 23rd Century that Vulcan discovered that the Romulans were the descendants of this lost, ancient tribe.

UNIFICATION ROMULAN STYLE

Spock tells Picard of earlier events. Years before, when he supported the Federation/Klingon peace proposal, James Kirk reluctantly supported him. They became entangled in a potentially disastrous affair. This time, rather than risk anyone else's life, Spock chose to go it alone.

Pardek, the Romulan representative, has assured Spock the unification proposal could pass the Romulan senate. If the Romulans pass the initiative, Spock will take it to the Federation. Pardek also tells Spock that the Proconsul of the senate will meet with him.

Spock has no reason to doubt Pardek. Spock's work for a peace initiative may have initially blinded him to the possibility of treachery by the Romulans. Pardek takes Spock to meet Neral, the Proconsul. Neral assures Spock that he'll support talks between Vulcan and Romulus.

Spock doesn't know the Proconsul and the military leaders plan to use the unification issue as a cover to invade Vulcan. They want to achieve unification in their own inimitable fashion.

SAREK'S LEGACY

When the Romulans capture Spock, Data, and Picard, Spock realizes Pardek's treachery. The Romulan commander, Sela, plans to have Spock send a message to Vulcan that a peace envoy is en route from Romulus.

The vessel will be accompanied by three cloaked Romulan ships carrying two thousand troops. They will seize control of Vulcan before anyone realizes what is happening.

Spock escapes his captors and dispatches a message warning the Federation. Exposed, the Romulan warbirds drop their cloak and destroy the troop transports to insure that the Federation cannot capture them.

Spock chooses to remain on Romulus as a hunted fugitive. Before Jean-Luc and Data leave, Spock mind-melds with Picard to get the message Sarek had left for him.

During all the years they lived, Spock and his father had never mind melded. When Spock melds with Picard it is evident the Vulcan is visibly moved by the final message he receives from his father.

THE VULCANS NEW ROLE

The only mention of Spock after this episode was in the sixth season's "Face Of The Enemy." A former defector returns to the Federation with a message from Spock about important members of the unification underground.

The Romulans are being smuggled out to defect to the Federation. Spock is still on Romulus working on behalf of unification.

Spock passed from science officer to ambassador to teacher. While he may act as ambassador again, Spock is now a spiritual guide. Romulans are the lost tribe of Vulcan who found a foothold far from home and preserved traditions Vulcans have left behind.

The bitter history of violence on Vulcan remains the way of life for Romulans. Now that could change with Spock to help lead his brothers and sisters into a transformed future.

Spock, the key figure of STAR TREK in the 23rd Century, has emerged in the 24th Century as a spiritual leader capable of transforming an entire people. He works to bring unification so the heritage of Surak of Vulcan can bring peace to another world.

"Sarek" proved the original STAR TREK could crossover into the 24th Century. Then Spock made his grand guest appearance in "Unification." Season five brought another old friend.

SCOTTY IN THE 24TH CENTURY: WHEN GENERATIONS CROSS

When STAR TREK—THE NEXT GENERATION began in 1987, many asked if the original STAR TREK cast members would appear on the new show. The official response was a resounding no. Five years later the tune had changed.

Sarek (Mark Lenard) had appeared in a crucial episode in season three; Spock had returned in season five. Bringing Scotty into the 24th Century STAR TREK universe in season six seemed the natural thing to do.

The storyline began when Michael Rupert pitched an idea for an episode. The editors weren't interested in his story ideas but did like his concept of a man trapped inside a transporter beam for many years.

Joe Menosky took the idea to Micheal Piller. He saw that it could bring back another original STAR TREK cast member.

The man-trapped-in-transporter-beam idea was bought from Michael Rupert and developed into a storyline by Ronald D. Moore. It was titled "Relics."

After it aired, Rupert tried to get story credit. Because he hadn't written a story, but only pitched an idea, the Writer's Guild refused to consider his request for an arbitration ruling.

Rupert continues to claim he came up with the idea for "Relics." Ronald D. Moore disputed Rupert's assertions in a letter printed in the June 1994 (Vol. 25 #3) issue of CINEFANTAS-TIQUE magazine.

DOUBLE MEANING

Scotty is found inside the transporter system of a shuttlecraft that crashed on the surface of an ancient Dyson Sphere.

A Dyson Sphere is new to TV science fiction but not unusual in print. It is an immense sphere built at an appropriate distance from a star. Inhabitants live on the inside of the sphere, taking advantage of natural solar energy in an area vastly larger than the surface of a single planet.

The Dyson Sphere in "Relics" was abandoned long before. On the exterior of this relic, they find Scotty—another relic.

Scotty is aboard a shuttle, the Jenolan, which crashed into the surface of the Dyson Sphere 75 years before. An away team investigates the shuttle as a matter of routine. They don't expect to find survivors.

The transporter array is still functional, activated into a closed loop inside the pattern buffer. The pattern buffer in a transporter insures that the person being transported will be reintegrated exactly the same as they were when they stepped onto the transporter pad.

Upon closer examination they find two beams in the loop, one of which has deteriorated too much to recover. The other appears intact. When they reintegrate the beam, they find Lt. Commander Montgomery Scott of the USS Enterprise. Scotty had been cycling through a transporter field for three quarters of a century.

WELCOME TO THE 24TH CENTURY

Scotty is just as he was when last seen in STAR TREK VI—THE UNDIS-COVERED COUNTRY. He's saddened that his fellow crewman didn't survive in the transporter loop but happy to learn he's been rescued by the Enterprise. At first he has no idea 75 years have passed.

This is a new use for the transporter. Even 24th Century transporters have never been shown to preserve a pattern for that long. The sixth season episode "Realm Of Fear" seemed to indicate a pattern degrades inside a transporter beam after a short time. Scotty engineered quite a feat, although the death of his comrade proves just how unreliable it was.

Scotty is out of touch with modern times, but not stupid. When he sees Worf in a Federation uniform, he quickly realizes more time has passed than he thought.

When he is examined in sickbay, Scotty tells his story. It is a poignant one. He had boarded the Jenolan on his way to the Norpin Five retirement colony.

Scotty can not resist poking about the starship, making comments and observations three-quarters of a century out of date. Finally Geordi explodes, complaining that Scotty is interfering with his job.

Scotty is taken aback. In the 23rd Century, he had been at the top of his field. Now his ideas seem hopelessly outdated.

AN ACQUIRED TASTE

"Relics" is the story of Scotty's rebirth. Even the subplot involving the Dyson Sphere relates to Scotty. He is instrumental in saving the Enterprise when it is trapped inside the ancient artifact.

Scotty explores this new Enterprise, and discovers Ten Forward. Scotty can't tell it isn't real booze because 24th Century drinks don't taste like 23rd Century tonics. He still loves his alcohol and isn't impressed by incredible simulations.

TOASTING THE DEPARTED

This episode mixes humor and drama as Scotty finds himself a man out of time trying to fit in. The new world is a mix of the familiar and the unfamiliar.

A starship is the best thing that could happen to Scotty. A starship shows

him how the familiar has advanced. He can concern himself with new technology rather than worrying about changes in culture or politics.

Scotty cannot escape his past. He uses the holodeck to recreate the bridge of the original starship Enterprise—the first Enterprise before it was refitted and changed. Originally this holodeck scene was to include images of the 1960s Kirk, Spock, McCoy, and the others. For various reasons, they settled for an empty bridge where a forlorn Scotty sits drinking and remembering departed friends.

Spock is still alive in the 24th century, although his personal mission to Romulus precludes a reunion. In Classic Trek, Scotty seemed to have the most in common with Spock. Both had scientific backgrounds. Spock clearly knew more about the engines of the Enterprise than anyone else on the bridge.

SCOTTY TO THE RESCUE

Geordi feels bad about his earlier outburst at Scotty. After he apologizes, the two return to the Jenolan to download the computers of the old shuttle.

Meanwhile, the Enterprise enters the Dyson Sphere. It may not be able to get out again.

Scotty rises to the challenge. Between Scotty's knowledge of the Jenolan's engines and Geordi's expertise with modern equipment, the two reactivate the Jenolan. It won't get them very far, but it doesn't have to.

The Jenolan flies after the impulse ion trail of the Enterprise, leading to two huge doors. They need to open the doors long enough for the Enterprise to escape. The plan works as Scotty and Geordi beam off the small ship just before the Jenolan is destroyed.

Classic Trek would have put Kirk in the shuttlecraft taking the last-second risk before being beamed off just in the nick of time. This time Scotty is the hero.

Scotty now decides he's not ready for retirement. He intends to explore this strange new world of the 24th Century first.

THE FUTURE OF SCOTTY

"Relics" is a much better story than "Unification." Scotty is far more central to the action than is Spock.

Spock doesn't appear until the last scene of the first part of "Unification." He then shares the stage with Data and Picard and an ongoing off-planet subplot.

Scotty's reactions to the 24th Century are important to the plot of "Relics." Spock aged naturally into the 24th Century while Scotty suddenly awakened into a brave new world.

There was discussion at Paramount about James Doohan joining the DEEP SPACE NINE cast. Nothing came of that, nor has he guest-starred on the series. No one connected to the original STAR TREK has graced the Promenade of Deep Space Nine. It seems only Enterprise personnel are good enough to consort with the legends from the 23rd Century.

Deep Space Nine offers opportunities for Spock and Scotty and other Classic Trek characters to fit in. Perhaps the future will bring the aboard the space station.

This is the history of the vessels named Intrepid, be they from Earth, Vulcan, or Rigel. These ships blazed a trail from the violent past into the 24th century.

SHIPS NAMED INTREPID

by Kay Doty

"Unshaken in the presence of danger; dauntless, courageous; having elegance."

These words define intrepid. It is not surprising a ship would be given such a name. It is not unexpected many worlds and nations used the name for vessels, beginning with the earliest voyages in history up to the 24th century.

RIGEL

Rigel's widely spaced, fourteen-planet star system presented an ideal challenge for the development of interstellar travel. Before Earth had launched Sputnik I in 1957, long before Zefram Cochrane had discovered the theories of warp-drive in 2061, and before Vulcan was reaching out to neighboring worlds, Rigellian scientists searched for a means of travel that would allow economic intercourse among the seven inhabited planets of the Rigel system.

Unknown to each other, space programs on Rigel VIII and Rigel X were developing similar possibilities. This was discovered when interplanetary probes established audio, and later, visual communications. Within two (Earth) years their combined efforts produced a ship that could travel between planets.

There were drawbacks: A trip to the outer reaches of the Rigel Star system took 9.17 years; the return trip even longer. Life support systems, in the early stages of development, were too unstable for use, and gravity control was still on the drawing boards.

Drones and simple androids were sent. The Rigellian people were excited, but the space-travel community knew their work had just begun. The artificial devices could not approach the abilities of

living beings. In the interim, they would have to do.

TECHNOLOGICAL BREAKTHROUGHS

While the little ship, Original, slowly made its way to the many worlds of Rigel, space scientists worked on many problems—and solved them. First came life support systems, followed by a means to overcome gravity with magnets and special boots.

Heavy bands, placed in strategic locations throughout the ships, prevented the crew from floating away from chairs, benches, beds and work stations. Finally live crews could be used, allowing a more efficient operation.

The ship builders were proud of their work, but the time required to travel the star system remained a barrier. This was solved by building a ship for each world, and developing an elaborate relay system. No ship had to travel further than the neighboring planet. This arrangement was

used until the development of the warp drive.

Shipyards on four of the inhabited planets worked at a fever pitch. Ships were built quicker than contractors had thought possible.

THE RIGELLIAN FLAGSHIP

Careful planning went into the selection of names for these miracle ships. Three were named for historical heroes, but the grandest of them all, the flagship built on Rigel IV, was named Intrepid.

The great day finally arrived when the first four ships were finished, crews selected, and cargoes loaded aboard, awaiting the signal to set sail. The flagship Intrepid would be the first to embark on the history making journey.

Bands played the national anthem of each world. Citizens dressed in their most colorful clothing and jewels. They plied planners, builders, and crews with huge platters of food and great jugs of drink. It was the greatest day in memory.

At last it was time! Millions watched in silent awe as the great ship rose from her base and hovered for a moment six meters above the ground. Then, with a short burst of sound, the engines engaged. Like a graceful bird, the Intrepid rose majestically into the atmosphere and out of sight.

The silence continued for several seconds as the ship disappeared beyond the last horizon. As if by careful orchestration, a tremendous roar rose from the throats of all on Rigel IV. They had just witnessed the beginning of a wonderful new era. Their world would never be the same again.

A FITTING CONCLUSION

The ruling council voted unanimously to declare a National holiday to be known forever as Intrepid Day. Ships were quickly added to the line. With an enhanced relay system, orders for goods placed on one world might reach another in as little as a month.

Many wished to visit the planets of their system. Some even elected to become residents of other worlds than their own.

Geologists could explore uninhabited worlds. Whatever their reasons for travel, a new tourism industry was born. After the invention of warp drive, the Rigel Star System became a galactic power.

The great ship Intrepid remained in service for over forty Earth years undergoing several rehauls before being retired from service. Newer, bigger ships were put on line. Alongside the men and women who served aboard the pioneering ship, Intrepid had earned a place of honor.

A park was built on Rigel IV. After being sprayed with a protective transparent coat, the Intrepid was ceremoniously moved to the beautifully landscaped park. A small museum chronicles not only the ship's history, but the adventures of her crews and her sister ships-of-the-line. Guided tours of the ship are conducted daily. Many guides are former crewmen. An honor guard is always present.

EARTH

Earth, the third and only inhabited planet in the Sol star system, is seventy-five percent water. Mankind was forced to build vessels to learn what lie beyond the seas. Great ships have been built since the earliest days of human history.

Small canoes propelled by long paddles made way for longboats, then sailing ships, and finally coal and oil driven vessels. The ships bore such inspiring names as Victory, Sovereign of the Seas,

Republic, Sea Witch, Flying Cloud, Thermopylae, Enterprise, and Intrepid.

A PRE-FLIGHT INTREPID

The first ship's registry began in 1914. As time passed, many countries enacted licensing and registration laws. These rules seldom covered all sizes and descriptions. There is no record of ship's names. To enumerate the ships throughout the ages that bore any one name is impossible.

Besides the United States, the United Kingdom, Germany, Brazil, and India have all launched warships bearing the name Intrepid. The best known, the Essex Class Aircraft Carrier, CV-11 Intrepid, was built at Newport News, Virginia in 1943. The ship weighed 27,100 tons, carried 103 aircraft, and 3,448 men and officers.

The Intrepid was a part of the Pacific Fleet in World War II. During the month of February, 1944, the Intrepid's planes strafed Ennuebing, helping to insure a safe ground landing by Allied forces at the battle of Kwajalein Atoll.

Late in the same month as the first strike on Turk Island, the Intrepid was struck by a torpedo leading to the loss of 28 men. Several compartments were flooded and the rudder jammed. Accompanied by seven ships, the Intrepid limped into Eniwetok at 20 knots, where several months were required to effect repairs.

This lengthy repair time was the result, in part, of a number of accidents that occurred while the ship was in drydock, earning her the nickname "The Evil Intrepid."

THE END OF THE WAR

Back in action by mid-October, 1944, along with the carrier Enterprise, the Intrepid was a member of Admiral William Halsey's Pacific Third Fleet. In the midst of a furious battle, the Intrepid was hit on October 29 by a Japanese Kamikaze with a loss of ten men killed and six wounded.

The damages were repaired within hours while the ship remained in the battle. On November 25, she again took a hit by a diving enemy plane. Sixty-nine men were lost when the plane plunged through the carrier's flight deck, starting serious fires. Despite the damage, she never lost propulsion and kept her anti-aircraft guns operational.

The Intrepid needed extensive repairs and, with a victorious end of the battle, again was headed for drydock. Back again by March 1945, the ship was a part of Vice Admiral Marc Mitscher's Task Force 38—again alongside the Enterprise. Both were hit during subsequent battles, but suffered only minor damage. They remained with the fleet in the drive on the Japanese homeland.

Fighting some of the heaviest sea battles, the Intrepid was hit again by another kamikaze on April 16 at the battle for Okinawa. The plane tore a 15 by 20 foot hole in the flight deck and started critical fires. Working feverishly, the crew had the fires out in under two hours, but the damage to her superstructure was too severe to repair at sea.

Ten men were killed and 87 wounded. The Intrepid and her weary crew returned to a Navy yard—her men reassigned after hard earned shore leaves. By the time her repairs were completed, the war was at last over—but the Intrepid, as unlucky as she was, had served her country well.

VIOLENT HISTORY

Another Intrepid, a luxury yacht belonging to a retired manufacturer of women's shoes, was the unlikely savior of seven prominent people.

The year was 2057 and Earth unexpectedly stood on the brink of a major world war. All nuclear weapons had been outlawed and destroyed half a century earlier—or so everyone thought—until a message was delivered to world leaders.

The threat couldn't have come at a worse time. Negotiations were in progress at Geneva to determine who would be awarded the contracts for developing the newly established Lunar Colony on Earth's only natural satellite. They weren't going well.

The German representative had been murdered. A minor official from New Zealand was arrested and charged with the killing, despite sketchy evidence.

Then the Chinese delegate became mysteriously ill, resigned, and returned home. Numerous fights, confrontations, threats, and an attempt at another murder followed—this time against the United States legate.

Evidence pointed to the British Prime Minister, but he had an unshakable alibi—he was in conference with the convention chairman and three secretaries. People traveled in twos and threes. Trust had vanished.

Many wanted to postpone the convention until the new problem was solved. The majority wanted the meetings to continue. World panic was just an eyeblink away.

NUCLEAR OUTLAWS

Two brothers, disgruntled office seekers, had acquired the materials necessary to build an arsenal of hydrogen bombs. Their purchases, made in widely scattered areas of the planet, had not gone completely unnoticed.

The computer, at the facility where two of the most vital ingredients were bought, had malfunctioned. By the time authorities were aware of the pair's complete shopping list, they had dropped from sight. The purchases had been made in 2054.

An extensive world-wide search for the unknown purchasers had produced nothing, even though their identities were known. One had charged the purchase to his bank credit line, and later bought airline tickets to Mendoza, Argentina. There the trail ended. Despite a months-long search by that country's rather formidable police force, no trace of the brothers was found.

As time passed and nothing was heard from the brothers, authorities let the incident slip from their minds. Then on July 4, 2057, the other shoe dropped!

While the Lunar Convention was in noon recess, the brothers, whose names were Leo and Arnold Cravlyn, placed a notice on the world's comm-net.

THE ULTIMATUM

"We have been denied our proper place in Earth's hierarchy long enough. It is unconscionable that we, two of the greatest minds in the world today, have been passed over as world leaders, by those of inferior abilities. This oversight must be corrected.

"We have developed five hydrogen bombs, which have been placed in the world's largest cities. All we have to do to activate them is push a button, therefore listen carefully.

"You, the world leaders, will appoint us the joint governors of the Lunar Colony. You will provide the Moonshuttle Britanica, stocked and fueled, to transport us there. Once we are safely at the Lunar station and have our protective shield in place, we will tell you where and how to dismantle the bombs. You have one week to make arrangements. Leo and Arnold Cravlyn. End of message."

The delegates entered a state of panic. The world population soon followed. No one knew if the threat was real.

Morale died after receipt of the message. There was a stream of threats, counter-threats, suspicions, and accusations in the conference hall.

THE DELEGATION

While the delegates argued, police departments searched for the Cravlyns. South American armies and police began a manhunt. Unity of world leaders was the only way to avert disaster.

It was left to a police sergeant in a small mountain town in Idaho to suggest a solution.

"Why not," he asked, "appoint a delegation of Tibetan Monks to heal the breach between the squabbling leaders, so they could continue their work on the contracts. Surely no one would suspect them of hidden motives. Then allow those of us who are trained police officers to do our jobs and find these bombjerks."

The delegates, now somewhat ashamed of their actions, agreed that the sergeant was right, but their nerves were suffering. Three days later, the world learned there were no bombs.

The brothers had tried to build one for over two years without success. On one occasion they demolished their lab, barely escaping with their lives.

THE PLOT THICKENS

They believed all they needed was the threat of a bomb, not an actual bomb. Yet they panicked when they learned about the Monks and their willingness to attend the convention—one of the brothers' many mistakes.

For some unknown reason, the Caravlyns decided the Monks would ruin their plans. After learning the flight plan of the airliner carrying the Monks, the two would-be governors fueled and armed their air-

craft with one of the most potent ground to air missiles available.

The jet plane, later found to be stolen, was sleek and fast. It was equipped for either water or ground landing. They planned to proceed to a spot approximately 100 miles off the coast of Ecuador, where the Monk's plane was scheduled to refuel.

Settling their own plane on the calm Pacific Ocean the brothers waited for the big transport to begin its descent, preparatory to landing. At that point they planned to shoot down the big plane. Then they made another mistake; they forgot to check for traffic!

The shoe manufacturer's yacht named Intrepid was about the size of a baseball stadium, an inconspicuous dot in the great Pacific Ocean. To make it even more difficult, the yacht was painted blue.

THE PLOT UNRAVELS

Seeing the small airplane bobbing in the water, the Intrepid's captain decided to investigate. Just as he pointed the yacht in the direction of the downed plane, he heard a loud report that could only be anti-aircraft fire.

The captain, with the owners consent, ordered full speed ahead. Two more shots were fired in rapid succession.

The brother proved no more expert with firearms than he'd been at building bombs. On the fourth try, the transport was hit badly enough to prevent the pilot from gaining altitude. He was in danger.

By then the Intrepid was nearly on top of the plane. With a nod from his boss, the Captain rammed it, knocking the shooter who had been sitting on the fuselage into the water.

In the confusion that followed, the brother in the drink was rescued. The brother remaining in the plane made the mistake of attempting to resist two of the Intrepid's crewman. When the short skirmish ended, he had a broken nose, a broken arm, and a decided desire to do no more resisting.

TRIUMPH OF THE INTREPID

The transport reached its destination safely, with enough damage that a new plane was required. The Cravlyns' plane was dented where the Intrepid's bow had struck, but still airworthy. A crewman from the Intrepid flew the small craft to port, where it was later used as evidence.

The Intrepid displayed her crumpled bow like a badge of honor as she was safely guided into the nearest port—at half speed—by her proud Captain.

The brothers were convicted on 22 counts each, sentenced to spend the rest of their lives in an isolated prison. Authorities found their secret camp high in the Andes Mountains, confiscated their equipment, and apologized to the locals who had been forced to do the brothers' bidding.

The Monks calmed the Lunar Convention and the delegates developed a fair agreement.

Mysteries unraveled: The German representative had been murdered by his wife's lover. The American was attacked to draw attention away from the murder. The Chinese emissary had over-indulged in rich Western food.

The Intrepid's owner, captain, and crew received tumultuous receptions at ports around the world as they continued their interrupted voyage. Again a ship named Intrepid lived up to her name.

VULCAN

Historians know little of the beginning and end of the wars that devastated Vulcan in the far distant past. Students of Vulcan history believe it has been 2,000 years since Surak taught logic and the subjugation of emotions as the means to end the killing.

A dark time haunts Vulcan history; a time when her people struggled for survival. The people were too busy rebuilding war-torn lives to keep records for posterity. Amidst the devastation, many doubted there would be future generations.

The majority looked to Surak as their last hope, but one small faction wanted no part of an emotionless life. This legendary group boarded three ships and set sail in a desperate search for a new home. They hoped they would not die forgotten in space but live on in the memories of their children and their children's children.

A few of the old ones, children when the journey began, survived to see the end of the odyssey. They were honored by being first to set foot on the new harsh planet.

ORIGIN OF THE ROMULANS

Many centuries passed before the hardy little group transformed their bare existence into the beginnings of an empire. Their fate was unknown until the mid-23rd century. Then the starship Enterprise, under the command of Captain James T. Kirk, encountered a ship from that previously unknown world, the Romulan Empire.

Vulcan Ancients of the Mount Sayla Temple believe the Intrepid was the flagship of the refugees. It was Vulcan's first venture into space.

This was confirmed many centuries later by the Romulan Commander of the Empire flagship. She was the victim of a Starfleet ploy to steal the cloaking device prototype for study. While in Federation cus-

tody, aboard the starship Enterprise, the Romulan Commander revealed that as a memorial to those brave pioneers, no Romulan ship was allowed to carry the name Intrepid.

Vulcan had developed space travel at least a millennia before Earth. The Vulcan's longer life span made it possible for a crew to travel into outer space and return without warp drive.

THE NEXT INTREPID

After its founding in 2161 at Babel, the United Federation of Planets commissioned a fleet of ships to explore space. Beings from member worlds manned the vessels.

Some ships carried mixed crews while others recruited staffs from a single world. The Intrepid, the first Federation science ship, was recruited solely from Vulcan.

The Intrepid was on her second five-year mission when the ship, with all hands aboard, was destroyed by a gigantic single-celled life form. The entity was later destroyed by the Enterprise with Commander Spock, Vulcan's best known Starfleet officer, playing a major role. This act of bravery nearly cost the Enterprise first officer his life.

FEDERATION SHIPS

Two other ships named Intrepid flew for the Federation. One was in dry-dock at Starbase 12 when Captain Kirk faced a Court Martial tribunal for the supposed murder of Commander Benjamin Finney.

Half a century later, another USS Intrepid received a distress call from the Klingon outpost at Khitomer. Romulans were attacking the outpost.

Despite traveling at warp nine, the Intrepid could not arrive in time to prevent the deaths of 4,000 Klingons. As the Starfleet officers searched Khitomer for survivors, they changed the future of the Klingon High Command, the Federation, and the Enterprise.

Warp field specialist Sergey Rozhenko found a terrified seven year old Klingon boy huddled under the bodies of his parents. The boy, Worf, had no known relatives. Sergey, and his wife, Helena, adopted the orphan.

THE KHITOMER LEGACY

The other survivor was Worf's nursemaid, Kahlest. Worf became the first Klingon to attend Starfleet Academy, and the first to serve on a Federation Starship—the USS Enterprise, under the command of Captain Jean-Luc Picard.

Years later, with Picard's help, Worf and Kahlest cleared Worf's father, Mogh, of treason at the Khitomer Massacre. They also preserved the line of command in the Klingon Council.

The unprovoked attack on the Klingon outpost was the most infamous massacre ever committed against a Federation member world. A ship named Intrepid was part of the tragic and historic incident.

In the 23rd Century STAR TREK, androids abound. Oddly, in the 24th Century shared universe of THE NEXT GENERATION and DEEP SPACE NINE they are rare.

ANDROIDS IN THE 24TH CENTURY

Androids appeared in such Classic Trek episodes as "What Are Little Girls Made Of?," "Return To Tomorrow," "Requiem For Methuselah," and "I, Mudd." The androids have different origins and different creators.

The only androids seen in 24th Century STAR TREK are Data and his kin. Other than Dr. Noonian Soong, no one in the 24th century has invented a working android.

Data has been part of THE NEXT GENERATION since the first episode. His "evil twin" was introduced in the first season episode "Datalore," when Dr. Soong's imperfect previous attempt at an android was discovered.

In the third season episode "The Offspring," Data uses knowledge from Dr. Soong to build a daughter. In the seventh season episode "Inheritance," Data meets the woman who assisted Dr. Soong in his experiments, only to discover she is also an android but doesn't know it.

Data was constructed by Dr. Soong on Omicron Theta IV. The colony on this world was later destroyed by the Crystalline entity.

When Data was found by a Federation survey ship, the android didn't know how he had gotten there. He knew nothing of the lab where he was created. The lab was not discovered until the episode "Datalore" in the first season of NEXT GENERATION.

No androids have appeared on DEEP SPACE NINE. Closest was a Replicant, something altogether different. A Replicant is an artificially created human being who can pass for the real thing. In this case the term clone would have been more accurate since he was a genetic duplicate of Miles O'Brien.

DO ANDROIDS HAVE HUMAN RIGHTS?

In 24th Century STAR TREK, the term android refers to an artificial humanoid. Dr. Soong may be the first human since Flint (a 23rd century scientist in "Requiem For Methuselah") to successfully create an android.

Data was accepted into Starfleet without his status as an android being secret, but it has generated controversy. In the NEXT GENERATION episode "Measure of a Man," Starfleet wanted to dissect Data to learn how to construct an android. He was put on trial to decide if he had the right to resist Starfleet's demands.

This began again when Data created Lal, his "daughter," in the NEXT GENERATION episode "The Offspring." Lal didn't have rights because she wasn't an official member of Starfleet. She was going to be taken into custody to be studied. This didn't hap-

pen because stress caused her to break down.

BUILDING THE BEST ANDROID

NEXT GENERATION revealed the composition of Data. His exterior shell, or skin, is made from Bioplast Sheeting. He also contains Molybdenum Cobalt Alloys. Then there is the Positronic Brain, the essential part.

Isaac Asimov invented the Positronic Brain in his novel, THE CAVES OF STEEL (1953). Not the real brain, of course, but an idea for robots that could pass as human.

THE NEXT GENERATION pays homage to Asimov. Gene Roddenberry and Isaac Asimov were friends for many years; it isn't surprising they shared ideas for NEXT GENERATION.

Androids consist of arcane elements. In the episode "The Most Toys," Data says he is mostly Tripolymer Composites.

He also contains Quadratanium.

Dr. Soong employed an Epidermal Mold for facial features. An Electromagnetic Synthomometer was used to reconstruct Lore, whose body was found on Omicron Theta IV.

The field is called Molecular Cybernetics. Dr. Noonian Soong learned it from Dr. Ira Graves.

The potential for androids was first revealed to the Enterprise on Graves World. The dying scientist transferred his consciousness into Data, supplanting the android's personality. When he began to lose touch with his own humanity, he jettisoned his consciousness. Data reclaimed the positronic brain.

THE DOCTOR IS ON HIS WAY OUT

Lore returned in the fourth season episode "Brothers," written by Rick Berman. Dr. Soong summoned Data, but accidentally also called Lore to his secret laboratory.

Soong had escaped the Crystalline Entity ravaging Omicron Theta IV. He had taken refuge on an isolated planet to continue his experiments.

The Doctor restored Data to normal and revealed a new microchip. The new chip could give the android the human emotions he craves.

Dr. Soong told Data he had been deliberately constructed without emotions. Data's predecessor, Lore, had been built with emotions. He had proven dangerous and destructive. The arrogant Lore had threatened the colony, and been deactivated in self-defense.

Soong now feels he has developed an emotions chip without dangerous side-effects.

Lore hates being deemed a failure by Soong. In a fit of jealousy, he overpowers Data and dresses in his Starfleet uniform.

The disguised android tricks Dr. Soong. The emotions chip is installed in the already unstable Lore.

He becomes completely unbalanced and attacks the ancient scientist, mortally wounding him. Lore escapes, but Data remains with his creator as the man breathes his last.

DATABORG

Lore disappeared until the season six cliffhanger, "Descent." During an attack by the Borg, Data experiences hate. He attacks and kills one of the Borg responsible for the destruction of the Federation outpost on Ohniaka Three.

The new, violent emotions scare Data. A diagnostic test reveals nothing.

Borg are a race who turn themselves into cyborgs. One captured Borg, Crosis, activates a device on its body that causes a negative emotional response in Data. The Borg are somehow involved with Data's newfound emotions.

Lore is behind it. He uses a signal to control Data. The Starfleet android frees himself from the effect before he does permanent damage to his Federation comrades. The confrontation ends with Lore turned off for disassembly.

ETHICAL CONSIDERATIONS

The only other android encountered by Data is Dr. Soong's female assistant. When the woman was critically injured in an accident, Dr. Soong transferred her consciousness into an android body but never revealed the change to her.

Data accesses her program, revealing the truth. The woman's android body will age normally until she "dies." Data would like to talk about their mutual android existence, but is forbidden to violate her privacy.

The woman's husband has no idea he's married to an android. No one discusses the moral implications. Perhaps by the 24th Century sex with a non human is not unusual.

NEXT GENERATION and DEEP SPACE NINE ignore many things. Although the holodeck was introduced on NEXT GENERATION, DEEP SPACE NINE took it several steps further, adding the holosuite and holo-brothels at Quark's Place.

Sex with holograms now appears possible. How different is that from sex with androids? Perhaps a future scientist can create perfect, compliant sex partners without human intellect.

Would they require human rights? What if robots were mass-marketed to satisfy the carnal desires of humanoids throughout the Alpha Quadrant?

Is Data a machine or a human intellect? Will his rights as a Starfleet officer continue to protect him? How will Data react to the exploitation of other synthetic constructions?

These are issues not yet faced. Perhaps one day STAR TREK will explore the social and moral questions.

It seemed the aliens of STAR TREK were virtually always humanoid because it's hard to add character to a cloud or an insect. Yet now, after more than 25 years of encountering one planet of humanoids after another, STAR TREK reveals it is all part of a master plan. . . .

ORIGINS OF THE SPECIES

The original STAR TREK often commented on the many humans discovered on the planets visited by the Enterprise. NEXT GENERATION and DEEP SPACE NINE haven't raised the issue, although most of the aliens continue to be humanoid. This mystery was explored and unlocked in the sixth season NEXT GENERATION episode entitled "The Chase."

The episode is written by Joe Menosky from a story by Ronald Moore and Joe Menosky. It is a mystery as neither viewer nor Picard know what the outcome of his search will uncover.

The deceptive title, "The Chase," isn't a clue to the outcome of the strange events that unfold following a visit to the Enterprise by Jean-Luc's old archeology teacher. Professor Galen always regarded Jean-Luc Picard as his prize student and was disappointed Picard insisted on entering Starfleet. Prof. Galen believed that Jean-Luc could have been a brilliant archeologist.

Prof. Galen makes one more attempt to sway Jean-Luc. It has been at least 30 years since Picard studied under the archeology professor, but Galen's enthusiasm is infectious. Galen's newest expedition is the chance of a lifetime.

The professor is astonished when Picard turns him down due to his obligations to Starfleet. He angrily cuts short his visit to the Enterprise.

A few days later, the Enterprise responds to a distress call from Prof. Galen, who is under attack by an Yridian vessel.

When the Yridians fire on the Enterprise, it responds in kind. The Yridian vessel explodes.

Yridians aren't common on STAR TREK. The last one had appeared in the episode "Birthright" when Worf encountered space station Deep Space Nine.

Jean-Luc is reunited with his old teacher who is rescued from the shuttlecraft. Galen has been mortally wounded and retracts his earlier criticism of Jean-Luc. In spite of the brief reconciliation, Picard takes it hard when the professor dies of his wounds.

THE GAME IS AFOOT

Why had the Yridians attacked his ship? Apparently they wanted information from the ship's computer files. Neither Data nor Geordi can figure out the significance of that information.

Captain Picard could have reported the incident to Starfleet, but he feels obligated to his old teacher. Had he accompanied Prof. Galen, he might have been able to save the man's life. He wants to complete his work.

When the professor lay dying, he had no time to tell Picard what it was all about. Since there's nothing of archaeological significance on Ruah IV, the

Enterprise goes to the professor's next planned stop—Indri VIII.

At Indri VIII they get a clue. Someone has devastated the planet's surface with a plasma weapon, destroying all life on that world. Clearly someone else is on the trail.

PIECE BY PIECE

The decimation of all life on Indri VIII allows Prof. Galen's computer files to be narrowed down to DNA codes. Galen has gathered DNA codes from 19 different worlds, some interlocked in what appears to be a prearranged pattern.

The design seems to fit a prearranged program. Unfortunately, the program cannot be determined until it is completed.

The chase begins when the Enterprise learns DNA codes are missing. Others also hunt for the linking fragments. They are prepared to violently obtain them, although no one really knows what the code will reveal.

Everyone thinks they know the purpose of the code. Some believe it is a super weapon; others that it is a vast power source. No one knows how a code links seemingly unrelated species on widely separated worlds.

The Enterprise encounters a Cardassian ship and a Klingon vessel also searching for the answers to Galen's mystery. Picard persuades them to pool their resources since they all have different codes. Working together they can solve the problem quicker. Reluctantly, the Cardassians and Klingons agree.

After combining efforts, one piece remains lost. Data finds the missing strand. Gul Ocett, the Cardassian, beams back to her vessel and fires on the Enterprise and the Klingon ship to disable them and to keep those ships from following her. Picard had anticipated this and Data had deliberately given the wrong information.

THE ANSWER AT LAST

Nu'Dag, the Klingon commander, agrees to accompany Picard to the true destination, the Vilmoran system. They learn that Gul Ocett follows close behind. No sooner do they obtain the final DNA code than a group of Romulans drop their cloak of invisibility.

Gul Ocett would rather destroy the last sample than allow the Romulans to obtain it, but Dr. Crusher secretly adds the sample to the others in a tricorder and a hologram appears. The hologram is that of a female humanoid from a race unfamiliar to any of them. The figure explains that their scientists seeded many worlds with life in their own image.

She adds, "It was our hope that you would have to come together in fellowship and companionship to hear this message. And if you can see and hear me, our hope has been fulfilled. You are a monument—not to our greatness but to our existence. That was our wish, that you, too, would know life and keep alive our memory. There is something of us in each of you, and so, something of you in each other. Remember us." The image stops speaking and the hologram fades out.

The Klingons and Cardassians are disappointed the message did not offer a tangible reward. Gul Ocett is annoyed the Cardassians and Klingons could have anything in common.

Everyone returns to their ships. The long chase is over; it was not a super weapon or a great power source.

THE TRUTH WILL SET YOU FREE

All is not lost. After Jean-Luc and Dr. Crusher beam back to the Enterprise, Capt. Picard receives a message from the Romulans. The commander of the warbird understood the message. Perhaps the Romulans will determine they and the

Federation have a basis for communication and understanding.

Just as Klingons and Federation achieved an understanding some 80 years before, Romulans and Federation may come to a meeting of the minds. Perhaps the common heritage and bloodlines will create a basis for understanding.

Earth of the Twentieth Century seems to indicate otherwise. Vulcans and Romulans have a shared heritage, but the worlds remain divided.

This is the core of Gene Roddenberry's STAR TREK—humanity rising above its primitive nature to throw off the choking yoke of violence and reach further out to the stars. The resolution of "The Chase" and its message of common ancestry behind disparate races and cultures is the essence of IDIC — Infinity Diversity in Infinite Combinations. This is the heart of STAR TREK both

in the 23rd Century and the 24th Century.

It's not all said and done, yet.

THE 24TH CENTURY HAS JUST BEGUN

The 24th century of STAR TREK is a strange new world with its own rules and a history far more complicated than the original STAR TREK. The universe of NEXT GENERATION and DEEP SPACE NINE have become closely interwoven, building on the original STAR TREK.

The two new series established their own cast of characters apart from the original STAR TREK crew. While some feel the characters on DEEP SPACE NINE are colorless, they forget that THE NEXT GENERATION was on for three years before they began memorable, character-defining episodes.

"Tapestry" and "Inner Light," the two best Picard stories, were in season six; "Family," the episode which first explored his background, was early in the fourth season. Comparatively, DEEP SPACE NINE isn't even off the launch pad yet.

The series began by building a convincing backdrop for the adventures. The basic philosophy is strongly influenced by Gene Roddenberry's personal vision since he created both the original STAR TREK and THE NEXT GENERATION.

DEEP SPACE NINE introduced a space station in a corner of space not as pristine and perfect as the starship Enterprise. Space station Deep Space Nine is gritty, more like something found in the STAR WARS universe where things are scratched and dented from daily use. The main characters are pure STAR TREK.

INSIDE OPERATIONS

Commander Sisko is a by-the-book commander who, unlike his predecessor, Gul Dukat, would never consider accepting a bribe.

Major Kira, a former Bajoran terrorist has mellowed in her new job as Bajoran liaison. She's even come to believe not all Cardassians are evil.

Jadzia Dax is a Trill. Despite being 800 years old, she's never been in a fight! In the second season episode "Blood Oath" she went to Kira to ask her what it's like to kill.

Julian Bashir is more than just the chief physician. He has a personality and a temper. In "Melora" he proved he has a sharp tongue.

Miles O'Brien, a few years Bashir's senior, sometimes acts as though their age difference is greater than it is. When they play racquetball, O'Brien emerges looking as though he's exhausted while Bashir is enervated.

O'Brien is funny and caring with his wife and child. He can get angry enough to hit someone. He seems more real than the other characters.

Odo holds back, commenting on things, remaining deliberately aloof.

There is much to be discovered about him still. He could emerge as the most popular character on the show—a snide version of Data.

MAKING NICE

Quark is portrayed as untrustworthy, resourceful, and someone who wears his heart on his sleeve. Two different episodes of DEEP SPACE NINE focused on sacrifices Quark made for a loved one. It's hard to take anything nasty he does very seriously. The show wants Quark both lovable and obnoxious.

Some fan letters consider DEEP SPACE NINE "too dark." They obviously don't know what dark is.

"Necessary Evil" showed flashbacks of the space station under the Cardassians. The station was clearly darker in the flashbacks than in the present.

Crime is not rampant on Deep Space Nine. There are no knifings in the corridors or criminals preying on merchants. Life is casual. Characters question the moral consequences of their actions. These are not the characteristics of a "dark" show; no character qualifies as an anti-hero.

The Cardassians, the villains of DEEP SPACE NINE, undergo a transformation in a recent episode. Gul Dukat went to Commander Sisko to help him prevent a war between Cardassia and the Federation colonies.

The Cardassians have begun to get more attention than the Bajorans who live on the planet around which the space station orbits. That may balance the attention the Bajorans got in the first year of the series.

THE KLINGON CONQUEST

The 24th Century version of STAR TREK overhauled the Klingons. The NEXT GENERATION transformed the Klingons from the simplistic presentation of the original STAR TREK into fascinating characters.

There was always something new to be discovered. They not only became allies of the Federation, but individuals of weight and presence important in any storyline favored with their appearance.

DEEP SPACE NINE took advantage of the changes to feature them in the second season episode "Blood Oath." The Klingons dominated virtually every scene in the story, even when they were off-stage.

THE ALIEN CONNECTION

The transformation of the Romulans has been more subtle. They've kept their edge, shown to be both villainous and valiant. Although they never appeared on DEEP SPACE NINE, the Romulans turned up in many interest-ing episodes of THE NEXT GENERATION, including "The Chase," "Face Of The Enemy," and "Pegasus," in the sixth and seventh seasons.

A Romulan should be included as a series regular in a future STAR TREK spin-off. Time and creativity have been lavished on the Romulans. It would be pointless to waste them in the background.

The Borg are powerful villains. The last war was fought with them in the season four premiere "The Best Of Both Worlds, Part II."

Since then, when they appeared in "I, Borg" in season five and "Descent" in season six, they were handled in completely different ways. Some fans feel the menace of the Borg has been severely diluted.

OUT THERE

DEEP SPACE NINE introduced the Gamma

Quadrant, a whole new realm of worlds. The Federation, in their role as caretaker of the space station and overseer of the welfare of Bajor, should organize expeditions into the Gamma Quadrant to contact the new civilizations.

Commander Sisko and the others wait aboard the space station for the aliens to visit them. Even then, in episodes such as "Move Alone Home," the aliens ignore the Federation.

Sisko doesn't lay down ground rules. Visitors should be treated politely but not allowed to do anything they please. The Federation takes an extremely passive position expressing minimal curiosity in the Gamma Quadrant.

Even after three million refugees arrived in "Sanctuary," the Federation didn't express interest. The Dominion conquered the world that enslaved the Scrians then allowed them to leave.

Perhaps the Federation maintains private contacts with the Dominion as the Ferengi do. Otherwise the disinterest about the Gamma Quadrant makes no sense.

THE NEXT GENERATION and DEEP SPACE NINE created a much larger STAR TREK universe of new characters, creatures, and ideas. The preference of Classic Star Trek or 24th Century Star Trek is no longer just one of characters aboard the Enterprise. There is far more now. STAR TREK isn't what it used to be—it is much more than that.

THE MAN WHO CREATED STAR TREK: GENE RODDENBERRY

James Van Hise

The complete life story of the man who created STAR TREK, reveals the man and his work.

$14.95 in stores ONLY $12.95 to Couch Potato Catalog Customers
160 Pages
ISBN # 1-55698-318-2

TWENTY-FIFTH ANNIVERSARY TREK TRIBUTE

James Van Hise

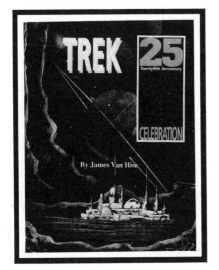

Taking a close up look at the amazing Star Trek stroy, this book traces the history of the show that has become an enduring legend. James Van Hise chronicles the series from 1966 to its cancellation in 1969, through the years when only the fans kept it alive, and on to its unprecedented revival. He offers a look at its latter-day blossoming into an animated series, a sequence of five movies (with a sixth in preparation) that has grossed over $700 million, and the offshoot "The Next Generation" TV series.

The author gives readers a tour of the memorials at the Smithsonian and the Movieland Wax Museums, lets them witness Leonard Nimoy get his star on the Hollywood Walk Of Fame in 1985, and takes them behind the scenes of the motion-picture series and TV's "The Next Generation." The concluding section examines the future of Star Trek beyond its 25th Anniversary.

$14.95.....196 Pages
ISBN # 1-55698-290-9

COUCH POTATO INC.   5715 N. Balsam Rd   Las Vegas, NV 89130   (702)658-2090

Use Your Credit Card 24 HRS — Order toll Free From: **(800)444-2524** Ext 67

THE HISTORY OF TREK

James Van Hise

The complete story of Star Trek from Original conception to its effects on millions of Lives across the world. This book celebrates the 25th anniversary of the first "Star Trek" television episode and traces the history of the show that has become an enduring legend—even the non-Trekkies can quote specific lines and characters from the original television series. The History of Trek chronicles "Star Trek" from its start in 1966 to its cancellation in 1969; discusses the lean years when "Star Trek" wasn't shown on television but legions of die hard fans kept interest in it still alive; covers the sequence of five successful movies (and includes the upcoming sixth one); and reviews "The Next Generation" television series, now entering its sixth season. Complete with Photographs, The History of Trek reveals the origins of the first series in interviews with the original cast and creative staff. It also takes readers behind the scenes of all six Star Trek movies, offers a wealth of Star Trek Trivia, and speculates on what the future may hold.

$14.95.....160 Pages
ISBN # 1-55698-309-3

THE MAN BETWEEN THE EARS:
STAR TREKS LEONARD NIMOY

James Van Hise

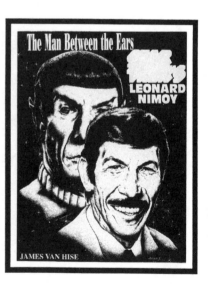

Based on his numerous interviews with Leonard Nimoy, Van Hise tells the story of the man as well as the entertainer.

This book chronicles the many talents of Leonard Nimoy from the beginning of his career in Boston to his latest starring work in the movie, Never Forget. His 25-year association with Star Trek is the centerpiece, but his work outside the Starship Enterprise is also covered, from such early efforts as Zombies of the Stratosphere to his latest directorial and acting work, and his stage debut in Vermont.

$14.95.....160 Pages
ISBN # 1-55698-304-2

BORING, BUT NECESSARY ORDERING INFORMATION

Payment:

Use our new 800 # and pay with your credit card or send check or money order directly to our address. All payments must be made in U.S. funds and please do not send cash.

Shipping:

We offer several methods of shipment. Sometimes a book can be delayed if we are temporarily out of stock. You should note whether you prefer us to ship the book as soon as available, send you a merchandise credit good for other goodies, or send your money back immediately.

Normal Post Office: $3.75 for the first book and $1.50 for each additional book. These orders are filled as quickly as possible. Shipments normally take 5 to 10 days, but allow up to 12 weeks for delivery.

Special UPS 2 Day Blue Label Service or Priority Mail: Special service is available for desperate Couch Potatoes. These books are shipped within 24 hours of when we receive the order and normally take 2 to 3 three days to get to you. The cost is $10.00 for the first book and $4.00 each additional book .

Overnight Rush Service: $20.00 for the first book and $10.00 each additional book.

U.s. Priority Mail: $6.00 for the first book and $3.00.each additional book.

Canada And Mexico: $5.00 for the first book and $3.00 each additional book.

Foreign: $6.00 for the first book and $3.00 each additional book.

Please list alternatives when available and please state if you would like a refund or for us to backorder an item if it is not in stock.

COUCH POTATO INC.   5715 N. Balsam Rd   Las Vegas, NV 89130   (702)658-2090

Use Your Credit Card 24 HRS — Order toll Free From: **(800)444-2524** Ext 67

ORDER FORM

___ Trek Crew Book $9.95	___ Number Six: The Prisoner Book $14.95
___ Best Of Enterprise Incidents $9.95	___ Gerry Anderson: Supermarionation $17.95
___ Trek Fans Handbook $9.95	___ Addams Family Revealed $14.95
___ Trek: The Next Generation $14.95	___ Bloodsucker: Vampires At The Movies $14.95
___ The Man Who Created Star Trek: $12.95	___ Dark Shadows Tribute $14.95
___ 25th Anniversary Trek Tribute $14.95	___ Monsterland Fear Book $14.95
___ History Of Trek $14.95	___ The Films Of Elvis $14.95
___ The Man Between The Ears $14.95	___ The Woody Allen Encyclopedia $14.95
___ Trek: The Making Of The Movies $14.95	___ Paul Mccartney: 20 Years On His Own $9.95
___ Trek: The Lost Years $12.95	___ Yesterday: My Life With The Beatles $14.95
___ Trek: The Unauthorized Next Generation $14.95	___ Fab Films Of The Beatles $14.95
___ New Trek Encyclopedia $19.95	___ 40 Years At Night: The Tonight Show $14.95
___ Making A Quantum Leap $14.95	___ Exposing Northern Exposure $14.95
___ The Unofficial Tale Of Beauty And The Beast $14.95	___ The La Lawbook $14.95
___ Complete Lost In Space $19.95	___ Cheers: Where Everybody Knows Your Name $14.95
___ ..doctor Who Encyclopedia: Baker $19.95	___ SNL! The World Of Saturday Night Live $14.95
___ Lost In Space Tribute Book $14.95	___ The Rockford Phile $14.95
___ Lost In Space With Irwin Allen $14.95	___ Encyclopedia Of Cartoon Superstars $14.95
___ Doctor Who: Baker Years $19.95	___ How To Create Animation $14.95
___ Doctor Who: Pertwee Years $19.95	___ How To Draw Art For Comic Books $14.95
___ Batmania Ii $14.95	___ King And Barker:an Illustrated Guide $14.95
___ The Green Hornet $14.95 ___ Special Edition $16.95	___ King And Barker: An Illustrated Guide II $14.95

100% Satisfaction Guaranteed.

We value your support. You will receive a full refund as long as the copy of the book you are not happy with is received back by us in reasonable condition. No questions asked, except we would like to know how we failed you. Refunds and credits are given as soon as we receive back the item you do not want.

NAME:_____

STREET:_____

CITY:_____

STATE:_____

ZIP:_____

TOTAL:_____ SHIPPING_____

SEND TO: Couch Potato, Inc. 5715 N. Balsam Rd., Las Vegas, NV 89130